Name _____ Class _____ Date _____

Concept Review

MW00844147

Section: Calculating Quantities in Reactions

Complete each statement below by writing the correct term or phrase.

1. All stoichiometric calculations involving equations use _____ ratios.

2. When solving stoichiometric problems, you must _____ the equation first.

3. Balanced equations give the _____ numbers of moles of substances.

4. _____ in chemical equations provide mole ratios that can be used as conversion factors.

5. The conversion factor for converting between mass and moles is the _____ of the substance.

6. In making calculations involving _____, you must convert volume to mass.

7. To convert from volume to mass, you can use the _____ of the substance as the conversion factor.

8. When calculating the number of particles, you can use _____ as the conversion factor.

In the blanks at the left, write the letter of the choice that best completes the statement or answers the question. Consider the following problem when answering:

What mass of sulfuric acid is required to neutralize 2.65 g of potassium hydroxide? The products of the reaction are potassium sulfate and water.

_____ **9.** What should you do first after reading the problem carefully?
   a. Estimate the answer.
   b. Calculate the molar mass of sulfuric acid.
   c. Write a balanced chemical equation.
   d. Convert all masses to moles.

_____ **10.** What should you do before setting up the problem?
   a. Determine the densities.
   b. Calculate molar masses.
   c. Convert all masses to moles.
   d. Estimate the answer.

| Concept Review continued

_____11. How should you check your setup?
    a. by recalculating molar masses
    b. by checking to see if the result will have the correct units
    c. by estimating the answer
    d. by writing a balanced chemical equation

_____12. What should you round off?
    a. the result of each step
    b. all data values
    c. only the final answer
    d. nothing

_____13. Which of the following is *least* likely to help you verify the final result?
    a. estimating the answer by using rounded numbers
    b. determining whether the answer is reasonable for the conditions of the problem
    c. rechecking all molar masses
    d. writing a balanced chemical equation

Answer the following items in the space provided.

14. Determine the number of grams of phosphorus formed for each 1.00 g of $Ca_3(PO_4)_2$ used in the production of phosphorus in an electric furnace.

$$Ca_3(PO_4)_2(s) + 3SiO_2(s) + 5C(s) \rightarrow 3CaSiO_3(s) + 5CO(g) + 2P(s)$$

$61.94 + 128 + 120.24 = 310.18g$ $61.94g$
        $1.00g$ $\times$

$$\frac{1.00}{310.18} = \frac{x}{61.94} \qquad x = \boxed{0.200g \ P}$$
$\div 5.01$

15. How many grams of aluminum chloride are produced when 18 g of aluminum are reacted with an excess of hydrochloric acid?

$$2Al(s) + 6HCl(aq) \rightarrow 2AlCl_3(aq) + 3H_2(g)$$

     $53.96g$ $266.66g$
       $18g$ $\times$

$$\frac{18}{53.96} = \frac{x}{266.66} \qquad x = \boxed{89g \ AlCl_3}$$
$\times 4.94$

Name _____ Class _____ Date _____

Concept Review *continued*

16. How many grams of ethanol, C_2H_5OH, can be made by the fermentation of 1150 g of glucose, $C_6H_{12}O_6$?

$$C_6H_{12}O_6(l) \rightarrow 2C_2H_5OH(l) + 2CO_2(g)$$

180.18 g   92.16 g
1150 g   x

$$\frac{1150}{180.18} = \frac{x}{92.16} \qquad x = \boxed{588 \text{ g } C_2H_5OH}$$

$\div 1.955$

17. How many moles of oxygen are required for the combustion of 25.5 g of magnesium?

$25.5 g = 0.524 \text{ mol}$

$$2Mg(s) + O_2(g) \rightarrow 2MgO(s)$$

2   1
0.524   x

$$\frac{0.524}{2} = \frac{x}{1} \qquad x = \boxed{0.262 \text{ mol } O_2}$$

18. How many grams of CO_2 are produced from the burning of 1.0 mol of amyl alcohol?

$$2C_5H_{11}OH(l) + 15O_2(g) \rightarrow 10CO_2(g) + 12H_2O(g)$$

2 mol   10
1.0 mol   x

$$\frac{1.0}{2} = \frac{x}{10} \qquad x = 5 \text{ mol} = \boxed{2200 \text{ g } CO_2}$$

19. How many moles of nitromethane are needed to form 500.0 g of chloropicrin, CCl_3NO_2, a chemical used in the production of insecticides?

$$CH_3NO_2(l) + 3Cl_2(g) \rightarrow CCl_3NO_2(l) + 3HCl(g)$$

| Concept Review *continued*

20. How many liters of oxygen are produced from the decomposition of 122 g of potassium chlorate? The density of oxygen is 1.33 g/L.

$$2KClO_3(s) \rightarrow 2KCl(s) + 3O_2(g)$$

21. How many grams of potassium chloride are formed by the decomposition of sufficient potassium chlorate to yield 3.4 L of oxygen? Remember that the density of oxygen is 1.33 g/L.

$$2KClO_3(s) \rightarrow 2KCl(s) + 3O_2(g)$$

22. How many liters of phosphine gas are produced when 910 g of calcium phosphide react with water? The density of phosphine gas is 1.517 g/L.

$$Ca_3P_2(s) + 6H_2O(l) \rightarrow 3Ca(OH)_2(s) + 2PH_3(g)$$

23. How many grams of air are required to complete the combustion of 93 g of phosphorus to diphosphorus pentoxide, assuming the air to be 23% oxygen by mass?

$$4P(s) + 5O_2(g) \rightarrow 2P_2O_5(s)$$

Concept Review *continued*

24. How many metric tons of carbon dioxide can be produced from the combustion of 5.00 metric tons of coke that is 85.5% carbon?

$$C(s) + O_2(g) \rightarrow CO_2(g)$$

25. If 100. mL of carbon disulfide (density = 1.26 g/mL) is burned completely, how many liters of SO_2 and of CO_2 are formed?

$$CS_2(l) + 3O_2(g) \rightarrow CO_2(g) + 2SO_2(g)$$

Skills Worksheet

Concept Review

Section: Limiting Reactants and Percentage Yield

Complete each statement below by choosing a term from the following list. Terms may be used more than once.

excess	product	limiting	stoichiometric
percentage	actual	theoretical	

1. A(n) _____ reactant is not completely used up in a chemical reaction.

2. A(n) _____ reactant is used up first and thus controls the

quantity of _____ that can be formed in a chemical reaction.

3. The reactant that runs out first is the _____ reactant.

4. The limiting reactant should be used in _____ calculations to determine the maximum amount of product expected.

5. Cost is a factor in selecting the _____ reactant.

6. In industry, the least expensive reactant is usually used as the

_____ reactant. In this way, the more expensive reactant is completely used up, while some of the cheaper reactant is left over.

7. The _____ yield is a way to describe reaction efficiency.

8. The percentage yield describes how close the _____ yield

is to the _____ yield.

9. The _____ yield must be measured experimentally.

10. The percentage yield figures can be used to predict what the

_____ yield will likely be.

Answer the following items in the space provided.

11. When 3.00 g of Mg is ignited in 2.20 g of pure oxygen, what is the limiting reactant? What is the theoretical yield of MgO?

$$2Mg(s) + O_2(g) \rightarrow 2MgO(s)$$

| Concept Review *continued*

12. When 32 g of O_2 reacts with 23 g of C_2H_5OH, what is the limiting reactant? What is the theoretical yield in grams of CO_2?

$$C_2H_5OH(l) + 3O_2(g) \rightarrow 2CO_2(g) + 3H_2O(l)$$

13. What is the limiting reactant when 154 g of Ag reacts with 189 g of HNO_3? What is the theoretical yield in grams of $AgNO_3$?

$$3Ag(s) + 4HNO_3(aq) \rightarrow 3AgNO_3(aq) + NO(g) + 2H_2O(l)$$

14. A student used 1.34 g of silver to produce silver nitrate. The actual yield was 2.01 g. Calculate the percentage yield.

$$3Ag(s) + 4HNO_3(aq) \rightarrow 3AgNO_3(aq) + NO(g) + 2H_2O(l)$$

15. To prepare the paint pigment chrome yellow, $PbCrO_4$, a student started with 5.552 g of $Pb(NO_3)_2$. The actual yield of $PbCrO_4$ was 5.096 g. Calculate the theoretical yield and the percentage yield.

$$Pb(NO_3)_2(aq) + Na_2CrO_4(aq) \rightarrow PbCrO_4(s) + 2NaNO_3(aq)$$

▎Concept Review *continued*

16. Determine the actual yield in grams of MgO when 20.0 g of magnesium is burned in air. The percentage yield of the reaction is 97.9%.

$$2Mg(s) + O_2(g) \rightarrow 2MgO(s)$$

17. Determine the actual yield of Fe_2O_3 when 10.0 g of iron(II) sulfide is burned in air. The percentage yield of the reaction is 88.1%.

$$4FeS(s) + 7O_2(g) \rightarrow 2Fe_2O_3(s) + 4SO_2(g)$$

18. Determine the actual yield in grams of CCl_4 if 175.0 g of Cl_2 reacts with methane. The percentage yield of the reaction is 75.4%.

$$CH_4(g) + 4Cl_2(g) \rightarrow CCl_4(g) + 4HCl(g)$$

Name _____ Class _____ Date _____

Concept Review

Section: Stoichiometry and Cars

In the blanks at left, write the letter of the choice that best answers the question.

_____ 1. How many moles of N_2 gas are generated from 0.50 mol of NaN_3 used
in an air bag? The reaction equation is $2NaN_3(s) \rightarrow 2Na(s) + 3N_2(g)$.
   a. 3.0
   b. 1.5
   c. 0.75
   d. 2.0

_____ 2. How many moles of isooctane will produce 6.0 mol of H_2O? The reaction equation is $2C_8H_{18}(g) + 25O_2(g) \rightarrow 16CO_2(g) + 18H_2O(g)$.
   a. 3.0
   b. 0.67
   c. 9.0
   d. 2.0

_____ 3. How many moles of carbon dioxide are produced when 5.0 mol of O_2
is used in the reaction $2C_8H_{18}(g) + 25O_2(g) \rightarrow 16CO_2(g) + 18H_2O(g)$?
   a. 80
   b. 0.40
   c. 1.6
   d. 3.2

_____ 4. How many moles of sodium oxide are produced if 0.5 mol of Fe is produced in the reaction $6Na(s) + Fe_2O_3(s) \rightarrow 3Na_2O(s) + 2Fe(s)$?
   a. 6.0
   b. 0.75
   c. 1.5
   d. 12

_____ 5. Why do designers of air bags use stoichiometry?
   a. to ensure that air bags inflate correctly
   b. to ensure that air bags do not overinflate
   c. to ensure that air bags inflate quickly enough
   d. All of the above

| Concept Review *continued*

Answer the following items in the space provided.

6. Use the concept of limiting reactants to explain why fuel-air ratios affect the performance of an engine.

_____

_____

_____

7. What mass of sodium azide must be included in an air bag to generate 68.0 L of N_2? Use 0.916 g/L as the density of nitrogen gas.

$$2NaN_3(s) \rightarrow 2Na(s) + 3N_2(g)$$

8. How many grams of air must react with 375 mL of isooctane for complete combustion to occur? Assume the air to be 23% oxygen by mass. The density of oxygen is 1.33 g/L, and the density of isooctane is 0.692 g/mL.

$$2C_8H_{18}(l) + 25O_2(g) \rightarrow 16CO_2(g) + 18H_2O(g)$$

9. Nitrogen dioxide from exhaust reacts with oxygen to form ozone. How many grams of ozone, O_3, could be produced from 4.30 g of NO_2?

$$NO_2(g) + O_2(g) \rightarrow NO(g) + O_3(g)$$

Skills Worksheet)

Problem Solving

Stoichiometry

So far in your chemistry course, you have learned that chemists count quantities of elements and compounds in terms of moles and that they relate moles of a substance to mass by using the molar mass. In addition, you have learned to write chemical equations so that they represent the rearrangements of atoms that take place during chemical reactions, and you have learned to balance these equations. In this chapter you will be able to put these separate skills together to accomplish one of the most important tasks of chemistry—using chemical equations to make predictions about the quantities of substances that react or are given off as products and relating those quantities to one another. This process of relating quantities of reactants and products in a chemical reaction to one another is called *stoichiometry*.

First, look at an analogy.

Suppose you need to make several sandwiches to take on a picnic with friends. You decide to make turkey-and-cheese sandwiches using the following "equation:"

2 bread slices + 2 turkey slices + 1 lettuce leaf + 1 cheese slice
$$\rightarrow 1 \text{ turkey-and-cheese sandwich}$$

This equation shows that you need those ingredients in a ratio of $2:2:1:1$, respectively. You can use this equation to predict that you would need 30 turkey slices to make 15 sandwiches or 6 cheese slices to go with 12 turkey slices.

Zinc reacts with oxygen according to the following balanced chemical equation:

$$2Zn + O_2 \rightarrow 2ZnO$$

Like the sandwich recipe, this equation can be viewed as a "recipe" for zinc oxide. It tells you that reacting two zinc atoms with a molecule of oxygen will produce two formula units of zinc oxide. Can you predict how many zinc oxide units could be formed from 500 zinc atoms? Could you determine how many moles of oxygen molecules it would take to react with 4 mol of zinc atoms? What if you had 22 g of zinc and wanted to know how many grams of ZnO could be made from it? Keep in mind that the chemical equation relates amounts, not masses, of products and reactants. The problems in this chapter will show you how to solve problems of this kind.

Problem Solving *continued*

General Plan for Solving Stoichiometry Problems

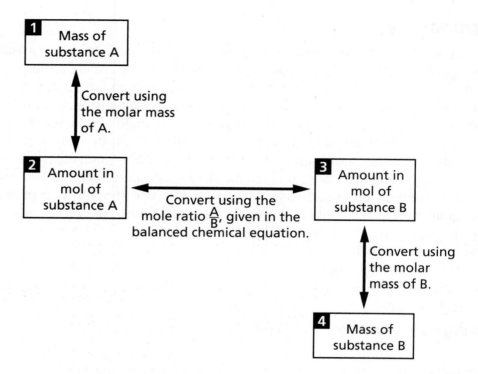

Problem Solving *continued*

Sample Problem 1

Ammonia is made industrially by reacting nitrogen and hydrogen under pressure, at high temperature, and in the presence of a catalyst. The equation is $N_2(g) + 3H_2(g) \rightarrow 2NH_3(g)$. If 4.0 mol of H_2 react, how many moles of NH_3 will be produced?

Solution
ANALYZE

What is given in the problem? **the balanced equation, and the amount of H_2 in moles**

What are you asked to find? **the amount of NH_3 produced in moles**

Organization of data is extremely important in dealing with stoichiometry problems. You will find that it is most helpful to make data tables such as the following one.

Items	Data	
Substance	H_2	NH_3
Coefficient in balanced equation	3	2
Molar mass	NA*	NA
Amount	4.0 mol	? mol
Mass of substance	NA	NA

* NA means *not applicable to the problem*

PLAN

What steps are needed to calculate the amount of NH_3 that can be produced from 4.0 mol H_2?

Multiply by the mole ratio of NH_3 to H_2 determined from the coefficients of the balanced equation.

2 Amount of H_2 in mol $\xrightarrow{\text{multiply by mole ratio: } \frac{NH_3}{H_2}}$ **3** Amount of NH_3 in mol

$$\underset{given}{\text{mol } H_2} \times \underset{mole\ ratio}{\frac{2 \text{ mol } NH_3}{3 \text{ mol } H_2}} = \text{mol } NH_3$$

COMPUTE

$$4.0 \ \cancel{mol \ H_2} \times \frac{2 \ mol \ NH_3}{3 \ \cancel{mol \ H_2}} = 2.7 \ mol \ NH_3$$

EVALUATE

Are the units correct?

Yes; the answer has the correct units of moles NH₃.

Is the number of significant figures correct?

Yes; two significant figures is correct because data were given to two significant figures.

Is the answer reasonable?

Yes; the answer is 2/3 of 4.0.

Practice

1. How many moles of sodium will react with water to produce 4.0 mol of hydrogen in the following reaction?

$$2Na(s) + 2H_2O(l) \rightarrow 2NaOH(aq) + H_2(g) \text{ ans: 8.0 mol Na}$$

2. How many moles of lithium chloride will be formed by the reaction of chlorine with 0.046 mol of lithium bromide in the following reaction?

$$2LiBr(aq) + Cl_2(g) \rightarrow 2LiCl(aq) + Br_2(l) \text{ ans: 0.046 mol LiCl}$$

Problem Solving *continued*

3. Aluminum will react with sulfuric acid in the following reaction.
$$2Al(s) + 3H_2SO_4(l) \rightarrow Al_2(SO_4)_3(aq) + 3H_2(g)$$
a. How many moles of H_2SO_4 will react with 18 mol Al? **ans: 27 mol H_2SO_4**

b. How many moles of each product will be produced? **ans: 27 mol H_2, 9 mol $Al_2(SO_4)_3$**

4. Propane burns in excess oxygen according to the following reaction.
$$C_3H_8 + 5O_2 \rightarrow 3CO_2 + 4H_2O$$
a. How many moles each of CO_2 and H_2O are formed from 3.85 mol of propane? **ans: 11.6 mol CO_2, 15.4 mol H_2O**

b. If 0.647 mol of oxygen is used in the burning of propane, how many moles each of CO_2 and H_2O are produced? How many moles of C_3H_8 are consumed? **ans: 0.388 mol CO_2, 0.518 mol H_2O, 0.129 mol C_3H_8**

| Problem Solving *continued*

Sample Problem 2

Potassium chlorate is sometimes decomposed in the laboratory to generate oxygen. The reaction is $2KClO_3(s) \rightarrow 2KCl(s) + 3O_2(g)$. What mass of $KClO_3$ do you need to produce 0.50 mol O_2?

Solution

ANALYZE

What is given in the problem?   **the amount of oxygen in moles**

What are you asked to find?   **the mass of potassium chlorate**

Items	Data	
Substance	$KClO_3$	O_2
Coefficient in balanced equation	2	3
Molar mass*	122.55 g/mol	NA
Amount	? mol	0.50 mol
Mass	? g	NA

* determined from the periodic table

PLAN

What steps are needed to calculate the mass of $KClO_3$ needed to produce 0.50 mol O_2?

Use the mole ratio to convert amount of O_2 to amount of $KClO_3$. Then convert amount of $KClO_3$ to mass of $KClO_3$.

2
Amount of O_2 in mol   *multiply by mole ratio*   **3** Amount of $KClO_3$ in mol
$\dfrac{2\ mol\ KClO_3}{3\ mol\ O_2}$

multiply by molar mass of $KClO_3$

4
Mass of $KClO_3$ in g

$$\overset{given}{mol\ O_2} \times \dfrac{\overset{mole\ ratio}{2\ mol\ KClO_3}}{3\ mol\ O_2} \times \dfrac{\overset{molar\ mass\ KClO_3}{122.55\ g\ KClO_3}}{1\ mol\ KClO_3} = g\ KClO_3$$

COMPUTE

$$0.50\ \cancel{mol\ O_2} \times \dfrac{2\ \cancel{mol\ KClO_3}}{3\ \cancel{mol\ O_2}} \times \dfrac{122.55\ g\ KClO_3}{1\ \cancel{mol\ KClO_3}} = 41\ g\ KClO_3$$

EVALUATE

Are the units correct?
Yes; units canceled to give grams of $KClO_3$.

| Problem Solving *continued*

Is the number of significant figures correct?
Yes; two significant figures is correct.

Is the answer reasonable?
Yes; 41 g is about 1/3 of the molar mass of KClO$_3$, and 0.5 × 2/3 = 1/3.

Practice

1. Phosphorus burns in air to produce a phosphorus oxide in the following reaction:

$$4P(s) + 5O_2(g) \rightarrow P_4O_{10}(s)$$

   a. What mass of phosphorus will be needed to produce 3.25 mol of P$_4$O$_{10}$?
   ans: 403 g P

   b. If 0.489 mol of phosphorus burns, what mass of oxygen is used? What mass of P$_4$O$_{10}$ is produced? **ans: 19.6 g O$_2$, 15.4 g P$_2$O$_4$**

2. Hydrogen peroxide breaks down, releasing oxygen, in the following reaction:
$$2H_2O_2(aq) \rightarrow 2H_2O(l) + O_2(g)$$

   a. What mass of oxygen is produced when 1.840 mol of H$_2$O$_2$ decomposes?
   ans: 29.44 g O$_2$

   b. What mass of water is produced when 5.0 mol O$_2$ is produced by this reaction? **ans: 180 g H$_2$O**

| **Problem Solving** *continued*

Sample Problem 3

How many moles of aluminum will be produced from 30.0 kg Al_2O_3 in the following reaction?

$$2Al_2O_3 \rightarrow 4Al + 3O_2$$

Solution

ANALYZE

What is given in the problem? **the mass of aluminum oxide**

What are you asked to find? **the amount of aluminum produced**

Items	Data	
Substance	Al_2O_3	Al
Coefficient in balanced equation	2	4
Molar mass	101.96 g/mol	NA
Amount	? mol	? mol
Mass	30.0 kg	NA

PLAN

What steps are needed to calculate the amount of Al produced from 30.0 kg of Al_2O_3?

The molar mass of Al_2O_3 can be used to convert to moles Al_2O_3. The mole ratio of Al:Al_2O_3 from the coefficients in the equation will convert to moles Al from moles Al_2O_3.

1
Mass of Al_2O_3 in g ◀—— *multiply by* $\frac{1000\ g}{1\ kg}$ —— Mass of Al_2O_3 in kg

multiply by the inverse of the molar mass of Al_2O_3 ↓

2
Amount of Al_2O_3 in mol —— *multiply by the mole ratio* $\frac{4\ mol\ Al}{2\ mol\ Al_2O_3}$ ——▶ **3** Amount of Al in mol

$$\overset{given}{kg\ Al_2O_3} \times \frac{1000\ g}{kg} \times \overset{\frac{1}{molar\ mass\ Al_2O_3}}{\frac{1\ mol\ Al_2O_3}{101.96\ g\ Al_2O_3}} \times \overset{mole\ ratio}{\frac{4\ mol\ Al}{2\ mol\ Al_2O_2}} = mol\ Al$$

COMPUTE

$$30.0\ kg\ Al_2O_3 \times \frac{1000\ g}{kg} \times \frac{1\ mol\ Al_2O_3}{101.96\ g\ Al_2O_3} \times \frac{4\ mol\ Al}{2\ mol\ Al_2O_3} = 588\ mol\ Al$$

| Problem Solving *continued*

EVALUATE

Are the units correct?
Yes; units canceled to give moles of Al.

Is the number of significant figures correct?
Yes; three significant figures is correct.

Is the answer reasonable?
**Yes; the molar mass of Al_2O_3 is about 100, so 30 kg of Al_2O_3 is about 300 mol.
The mole ratio of $Al:Al_2O_3$ is 2:1, so the answer should be about 600 mol Al.**

Practice

1. Sodium carbonate reacts with nitric acid according to the following equation.

$$Na_2CO_3(s) + 2HNO_3 \rightarrow 2NaNO_3 + CO_2 + H_2O$$

a. How many moles of Na_2CO_3 are required to produce 100.0 g of $NaNO_3$?
ans: 0.5882 mol Na_2CO_3

b. If 7.50 g of Na_2CO_3 reacts, how many moles of CO_2 are produced? **ans:
0.0708 mol CO_2**

2. Hydrogen is generated by passing hot steam over iron, which oxidizes to form Fe_3O_4, in the following equation.

$$3Fe(s) + 4H_2O(g) \rightarrow 4H_2(g) + Fe_3O_4(s)$$

a. If 625 g of Fe_3O_4 is produced in the reaction, how many moles of hydrogen are produced at the same time? **ans: 10.8 mol H_2**

b. How many moles of iron would be needed to generate 27 g of hydrogen?
ans: 10. mol Fe

Sample Problem 4

Methane burns in air by the following reaction:

$$CH_4(g) + 2O_2(g) \rightarrow CO_2(g) + 2H_2O(g)$$

What mass of water is produced by burning 500. g of methane?

Solution

ANALYZE

What is given in the problem?   **the mass of methane in grams**

What are you asked to find?   **the mass of water produced**

Items	Data	
Substance	CH_4	H_2O
Coefficient in balanced equation	1	2
Molar mass	16.05 g/mol	18.02 g/mol
Amount	? mol	? mol
Mass	500. g	? g

PLAN

What steps are needed to calculate the mass of H_2O produced from the burning of 500. g of CH_4?

Convert grams of CH_4 to moles CH_4 by using the molar mass of CH_4. Use the mole ratio from the balanced equation to determine moles H_2O from moles CH_4. Use the molar mass of H_2O to calculate grams H_2O.

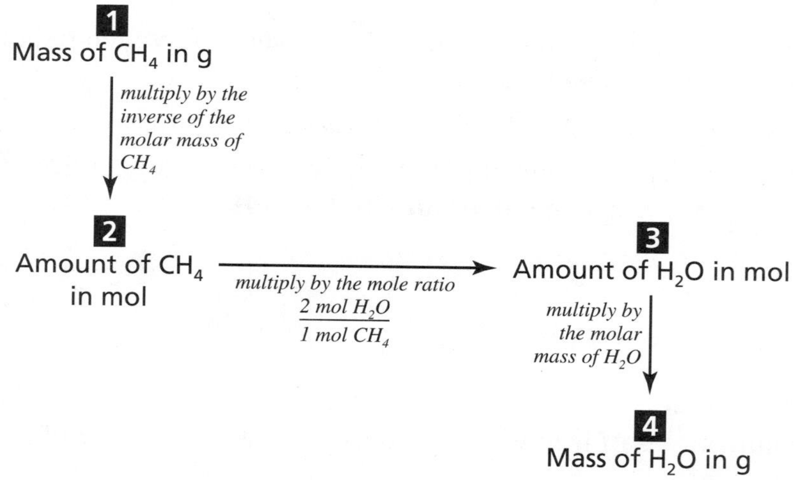

1
Mass of CH$_4$ in g

multiply by the inverse of the molar mass of CH$_4$

2
Amount of CH$_4$ in mol
multiply by the mole ratio $\frac{2\ mol\ H_2O}{1\ mol\ CH_4}$

3
Amount of H$_2$O in mol

multiply by the molar mass of H$_2$O

4
Mass of H$_2$O in g

$$\text{g } \overset{given}{CH_4} \times \frac{\overset{\frac{1}{molar\ mass\ CH_4}}{1 \text{ mol } CH_4}}{16.05 \text{ g } CH_4} \times \frac{\overset{mole\ ratio}{2 \text{ mol } H_2O}}{1 \text{ mol } CH_4} \times \frac{\overset{molar\ mass\ H_2O}{18.02 \text{ g } H_2O}}{1 \text{ mol } H_2O} = \text{g } H_2O$$

Problem Solving *continued*

COMPUTE

$$500. \text{ g } \cancel{CH_4} \times \frac{1 \text{ mol } \cancel{CH_4}}{16.05 \text{ g } \cancel{CH_4}} \times \frac{2 \text{ mol } \cancel{H_2O}}{1 \text{ mol } \cancel{CH_4}} \times \frac{18.02 \text{ g } H_2O}{1 \text{ mol } \cancel{H_2O}} = 1.12 \times 10^3 \text{ g } H_2O$$

EVALUATE

Are the units correct?

Yes; mass of H_2O was required, and units canceled to give grams H_2O.

Is the number of significant figures correct?

Yes; three significant figures is correct because the mass of CH_4 was given to three significant figures.

Is the answer reasonable?

Yes; CH_4 and H_2O have similar molar masses, and twice as many moles of H_2O are produced as moles CH_4 burned. So, you would expect to get a little more than 1000 g of H_2O.

Practice

1. Calculate the mass of silver bromide produced from 22.5 g of silver nitrate in the following reaction:

$$2AgNO_3(aq) + MgBr_2(aq) \rightarrow 2AgBr(s) + Mg(NO_3)_2(aq) \text{ ans: } \textbf{24.9 g AgBr}$$

2. What mass of acetylene, C_2H_2, will be produced from the reaction of 90. g of calcium carbide, CaC_2, with water in the following reaction?

$$CaC_2(s) + 2H_2O(l) \rightarrow C_2H_2(g) + Ca(OH)_2(s) \text{ ans: } \textbf{37 g C}_2\textbf{H}_2$$

3. Chlorine gas can be produced in the laboratory by adding concentrated hydrochloric acid to manganese(IV) oxide in the following reaction:

$$MnO_2(s) + 4HCl(aq) \rightarrow MnCl_2(aq) + 2H_2O(l) + Cl_2(g)$$

a. Calculate the mass of MnO_2 needed to produce 25.0 g of Cl_2. **ans: 30.7 g MnO_2**

b. What mass of $MnCl_2$ is produced when 0.091 g of Cl_2 is generated?
ans: 0.16 g $MnCl_2$

Additional Problems

1. How many moles of ammonium sulfate can be made from the reaction of 30.0 mol of NH_3 with H_2SO_4 according to the following equation?

$$2NH_3 + H_2SO_4 \rightarrow (NH_4)_2SO_4$$

2. In a very violent reaction called a thermite reaction, aluminum metal reacts with iron(III) oxide to form iron metal and aluminum oxide according to the following equation:

$$Fe_2O_3 + 2Al \rightarrow 2Fe + Al_2O_3$$

a. What mass of Al will react with 150 g of Fe_2O_3?

b. If 0.905 mol Al_2O_3 is produced in the reaction, what mass of Fe is produced?

c. How many moles of Fe_2O_3 will react with 99.0 g of Al?

3. As you saw in Sample Problem 1, the reaction $N_2(g) + 3H_2(g) \rightarrow 2NH_3(g)$ is used to produce ammonia commercially. If 1.40 g of N_2 are used in the reaction, how many grams of H_2 will be needed?

4. What mass of sulfuric acid, H_2SO_4, is required to react with 1.27 g of potassium hydroxide, KOH? The products of this reaction are potassium sulfate and water.

5. Ammonium hydrogen phosphate, $(NH_4)_2HPO_4$, a common fertilizer, is made from reacting phosphoric acid, H_3PO_4, with ammonia.

a. Write the equation for this reaction.

b. If 10.00 g of ammonia react, how many moles of fertilizer will be produced?

c. What mass of ammonia will react with 2800 kg of H_3PO_4?

6. The following reaction shows the synthesis of zinc citrate, a ingredient in toothpaste, from zinc carbonate and citric acid.

$$3ZnCO_3(s) + 2C_6H_8O_7(aq) \rightarrow Zn_3(C_6H_5O_7)_2(aq) + 3H_2O(l) + 3CO_2(g)$$

a. How many moles of $ZnCO_3$ and $C_6H_8O_7$ are required to produce 30.0 mol of $Zn_3(C_6H_5O_7)_2$?

b. What quantities, in kilograms, of H_2O and CO_2 are produced by the reaction of 500. mol of citric acid?

7. Methyl butanoate, an oily substance with a strong fruity fragrance, can be made by reacting butanoic acid with methanol according to the following equation:

$$C_3H_7COOH + CH_3OH \rightarrow C_3H_7COOCH_3 + H_2O$$

a. What mass of methyl butanoate is produced from the reaction of 52.5 g of butanoic acid?

b. In order to purify methyl butanoate, water must be removed. What mass of water is produced from the reaction of 5800. g of methanol?

8. Ammonium nitrate decomposes to yield nitrogen gas, water, and oxygen gas in the following reaction:

$$2NH_4NO_3 \rightarrow 2N_2 + O_2 + 4H_2O$$

a. How many moles of nitrogen gas are produced when 36.0 g of NH_4NO_3 reacts?

b. If 7.35 mol of H_2O are produced in this reaction, what mass of NH_4NO_3 reacted?

9. Lead(II) nitrate reacts with potassium iodide to produce lead(II) iodide and potassium nitrate. If 1.23 mg of lead nitrate are consumed, what is the mass of the potassium nitrate produced?

10. A car battery produces electrical energy with the following chemical reaction:

$$Pb(s) + PbO_2(s) + 2H_2SO_4(aq) \rightarrow 2PbSO_4(s) + 2H_2O(l)$$

If the battery loses 0.34 kg of lead in this reaction, how many moles of lead(II) sulfate are produced?

11. In a space shuttle, the CO_2 that the crew exhales is removed from the air by a reaction within canisters of lithium hydroxide. On average, each astronaut exhales about 20.0 mol of CO_2 daily. What mass of water will be produced when this amount reacts with LiOH? The other product of the reaction is Li_2CO_3.

12. Water is sometimes removed from the products of a reaction by placing them in a closed container with excess P_4O_{10}. Water is absorbed by the following reaction:

$$P_4O_{10} + 6H_2O \rightarrow 4H_3PO_4$$

a. What mass of water can be absorbed by 1.00×10^2 g of P_4O_{10}?

b. If the P_4O_{10} in the container absorbs 0.614 mol of water, what mass of H_3PO_4 is produced?

c. If the mass of the container of P_4O_{10} increases from 56.64 g to 63.70 g, how many moles of water are absorbed?

13. Ethanol, C_2H_5OH, is considered a clean fuel because it burns in oxygen to produce carbon dioxide and water with few trace pollutants. If 95.0 g of H_2O are produced during the combustion of ethanol, how many grams of ethanol were present at the beginning of the reaction?

14. Sulfur dioxide is one of the major contributors to acid rain. Sulfur dioxide can react with oxygen and water in the atmosphere to form sulfuric acid, as shown in the following equation:

$$2H_2O(l) + O_2(g) + 2SO_2(g) \rightarrow 2H_2SO_4(aq)$$

If 50.0 g of sulfur dioxide from pollutants reacts with water and oxygen found in the air, how many grams of sulfuric acid can be produced? How many grams of oxygen are used in the process?

❚ Problem Solving *continued*

15. When heated, sodium bicarbonate, $NaHCO_3$, decomposes into sodium carbonate, Na_2CO_3, water, and carbon dioxide. If 5.00 g of $NaHCO_3$ decomposes, what is the mass of the carbon dioxide produced?

16. A reaction between hydrazine, N_2H_4, and dinitrogen tetroxide, N_2O_4, has been used to launch rockets into space. The reaction produces nitrogen gas and water vapor.

a. Write a balanced chemical equation for this reaction.

b. What is the mole ratio of N_2O_4 to N_2?

c. How many moles of N_2 will be produced if 20 000 mol of N_2H_4 are used by a rocket?

d. How many grams of H_2O are made when 450. kg of N_2O_4 are consumed?

17. Joseph Priestley is credited with the discovery of oxygen. He produced O_2 by heating mercury(II) oxide, HgO, to decompose it into its elements. How many moles of oxygen could Priestley have produced if he had decomposed 517.84 g of mercury oxide?

18. Iron(III) chloride, $FeCl_3$, can be made by the reaction of iron with chlorine gas. How much iron, in grams, will be needed to completely react with 58.0 g of Cl_2?

19. Sodium sulfide and cadmium nitrate undergo a double-replacement reaction, as shown by the following equation:

$$Na_2S + Cd(NO_3)_2 \rightarrow 2NaNO_3 + CdS$$

What is the mass, in milligrams, of cadmium sulfide that can be made from 5.00 mg of sodium sulfide?

20. Potassium permanganate and glycerin react explosively according to the following equation:

$$14KMnO_4 + 4C_3H_5(OH)_3 \rightarrow 7K_2CO_3 + 7Mn_2O_3 + 5CO_2 + 16H_2O$$

a. How many moles of carbon dioxide can be produced from 4.44 mol of $KMnO_4$?

b. If 5.21 g of H_2O are produced, how many moles of glycerin, $C_3H_5(OH)_3$, were used?

c. If 3.39 mol of potassium carbonate are made, how many grams of manganese(III) oxide are also made?

d. How many grams of glycerin will be needed to react with 50.0 g of $KMnO_4$? How many grams of CO_2 will be produced in the same reaction?

21. Calcium carbonate found in limestone and marble reacts with hydrochloric acid to form calcium chloride, carbon dioxide, and water according to the following equation:

$$CaCO_3(s) + 2HCl(aq) \rightarrow CaCl_2(aq) + CO_2(g) + H_2O(l)$$

a. What mass of HCl will be needed to produce 5.00×10^3 kg of $CaCl_2$?

b. What mass of CO_2 could be produced from the reaction of 750 g of $CaCO_3$?

22. The fuel used to power the booster rockets on the space shuttle is a mixture of aluminum metal and ammonium perchlorate. The following balanced equation represents the reaction of these two ingredients:

$$3Al(s) + 3NH_4ClO_4(s) \rightarrow Al_2O_3(s) + AlCl_3(g) + 3NO(g) + 6H_2O(g)$$

a. If 1.50×10^5 g of Al react, what mass of NH_4ClO_4, in grams, is required?

b. If aluminum reacts with 620 kg of NH_4ClO_4, what mass of nitrogen monoxide is produced?

23. Phosphoric acid is typically produced by the action of sulfuric acid on rock that has a high content of calcium phosphate according to the following equation:

$$3H_2SO_4 + Ca_3(PO_4)_2 + 6H_2O \rightarrow 3[CaSO_4 \cdot 2H_2O] + 2H_3PO_4$$

a. If 2.50×10^5 kg of H_2SO_4 react, how many moles of H_3PO_4 can be made?

b. What mass of calcium sulfate dihydrate is produced by the reaction of 400. kg of calcium phosphate?

c. If the rock being used contains 78.8% $Ca_3(PO_4)_2$, how many metric tons of H_3PO_4 can be produced from 68 metric tons of rock?

24. Rusting of iron occurs in the presence of moisture according to the following equation:

$$4Fe(s) + 3O_2(g) \rightarrow 2Fe_2O_3(s)$$

Suppose that 3.19% of a heap of steel scrap with a mass of 1650 kg rusts in a year. What mass will the heap have after one year of rusting?

Skills Worksheet

Problem Solving

Limiting Reactants

At the beginning of Chapter 8, a comparison was made between solving stoichiometry problems and making turkey sandwiches. Look at the sandwich recipe once more:

2 bread slices + 2 turkey slices + 1 lettuce leaf + 1 cheese slice →
1 turkey-and-cheese sandwich

If you have 24 slices of turkey, you can make 12 sandwiches at 2 slices per sandwich *if you have enough of all the other ingredients*. If, however, you have only 16 slices of bread, you can make only 8 sandwiches, even though you may an ample supply of the other ingredients. The bread is the *limiting* ingredient that prevents you from making more than 8 sandwiches.

The same idea applies to chemical reactions. Look at a reaction used to generate hydrogen gas in the laboratory:

$$Zn(s) + H_2SO_4(aq) \rightarrow ZnSO_4(aq) + H_2(g)$$

The balanced equation tells you that 1 mol Zn reacts with 1 mol H_2SO_4 to produce 1 mol $ZnSO_2$ and 1 mol H_2. Suppose you have 1 mol Zn and 5 mol H_2SO_4. What will happen, and what will you get? Only 1 mol of H_2SO_4 will react and only 1 mol of each of the products will be produced because only 1 mol Zn is available to react. In this situation, zinc is the limiting reactant. When it is used up the reaction stops even though more H_2SO_4 is available.

It is difficult to directly observe molar amounts of reactants as they are used up. It is much easier to determine when a certain mass of a reactant has been completely used. Use molar masses to restate the equation in terms of mass, as follows:

$$65.39 \text{ g Zn} + 98.09 \text{ g } H_2SO_4 \rightarrow 161.46 \text{ g } ZnSO_4 + 2.02 \text{ g } H_2$$

This version of the equation tells you that zinc and sulfuric acid will *always* react in a mass ratio of 65.39 g of Zn : 98.09 g of H_2SO_4 or 0.667 g of Zn : 1.000 g of H_2SO_4. If you have 65.39 g of Zn but only 87.55 g of H_2SO_4, you will not be able to make 2.02 g of hydrogen. Sulfuric acid will be the limiting reactant, preventing the zinc from reacting completely. Suppose you place 20 g of zinc and 100 g of sulfuric acid into a flask. Which would be used up first? In other words, is the limiting reactant zinc or sulfuric acid? How much of each product will be produced? The sample problems in this chapter will show you how to answer these questions.

Problem Solving *continued*

General Plan for Solving Limiting Reactant Problems

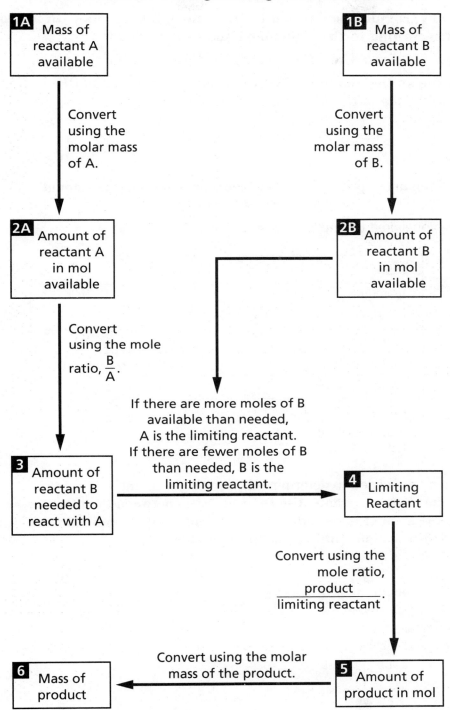

| Problem Solving *continued*

Sample Problem 1

Calcium hydroxide, used to neutralize acid spills, reacts with hydrochloric acid according to the following equation:

$$Ca(OH)_2 + 2HCl \rightarrow CaCl_2 + 2H_2O$$

If you have spilled 6.3 mol of HCl and put 2.8 mol of $Ca(OH)_2$ on it, which substance is the limiting reactant?

Solution
ANALYZE

What is given in the problem? **the balanced equation, the amounts of $Ca(OH)_2$ and HCl in moles**

What are you asked to find? **the limiting reactant**

Items	Data	
Reactant	$Ca(OH)_2$	HCl
Coefficient in balanced equation	1	2
Molar mass	NA*	NA
Amount of reactant	2.8 mol	6.3 mol
Mass of reactant	NA	NA
Limiting reactant	?	?

* not applicable to the problem

PLAN

What steps are needed to determine the limiting reactant?

Choose one of the reactants. Use the mole ratio between the two reactants to compute the amount of the other reactant that would be needed to react with it. Compare that amount with the amount available.

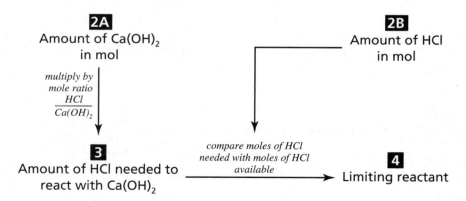

Choose one of the reactants, for instance, $Ca(OH)_2$

$$\text{mol } \overset{given}{\text{Ca(OH)}_2} \times \frac{\overset{mole\ ratio}{2 \text{ mol HCl}}}{1 \text{ mol Ca(OH)}_2} = \text{mol HCl needed}$$

COMPUTE

$$2.8 \text{ mol Ca(OH)}_2 \times \frac{2 \text{ mol HCl}}{1 \text{ mol Ca(OH)}_2} = 5.6 \text{ mol HCl needed}$$

The computation shows that more HCl (6.3 mol) is available than is needed (5.6 mol) to react with the 2.8 mol $Ca(OH)_2$ available. Therefore, HCl is present in excess, making $Ca(OH)_2$ the limiting reactant.

EVALUATE

Is the answer reasonable?

Yes; you can see that 6.3 mol HCl is more than is needed to react with 2.8 mol $Ca(OH)_2$.

Practice

1. Aluminum oxidizes according to the following equation:

$$4Al + 3O_2 \rightarrow 2Al_2O_3$$

Powdered Al (0.048 mol) is placed into a container containing 0.030 mol O_2. What is the limiting reactant? **ans: O_2**

Problem Solving *continued*

Sample Problem 2

Chlorine can replace bromine in bromide compounds forming a chloride compound and elemental bromine. The following equation is an example of this reaction.

$$2KBr(aq) + Cl_2(aq) \rightarrow 2KCl(aq) + Br_2(l)$$

When 0.855 g of Cl_2 and 3.205 g of KBr are mixed in solution, which is the limiting reactant? How many grams of Br_2 are formed?

Solution

ANALYZE

What is given in the problem? **the balanced equation, and the masses of Cl_2 and KBr available**

What are you asked to find? **which reactant is limiting, and the mass of Br_2 produced**

Items	Data		
Substance	KBr	Cl_2	Br_2
Coefficient in balanced equation	2	1	1
Molar mass*	119.00 g/mol	70.90 g/mol	159.80 g/mol
Amount of substance	? mol	? mol	? mol
Mass of substance	3.205 g	0.855 g	? g
Limiting reactant	?	?	NA

*determined from the periodic table

PLAN

What steps are needed to determine the limiting reactant?
Convert mass of each reactant to amount in moles. Choose one of the reactants. Compute the amount of the other reactant needed. Compare that with the amount available.

What steps are needed to determine the mass of Br_2 produced in the reaction?
Use amount of the limiting reactant and the mole ratio given in the equation to determine the amount of Br_2. Convert the amount of Br_2 to the mass of Br_2 using the molar mass.

Problem Solving *continued*

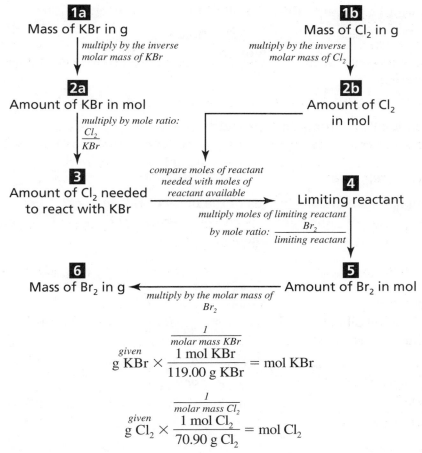

1a
Mass of KBr in g
multiply by the inverse molar mass of KBr

1b
Mass of Cl_2 in g
multiply by the inverse molar mass of Cl_2

2a
Amount of KBr in mol
multiply by mole ratio:
$\dfrac{Cl_2}{KBr}$

2b
Amount of Cl_2 in mol

3
Amount of Cl_2 needed to react with KBr

compare moles of reactant needed with moles of reactant available

4
Limiting reactant
multiply moles of limiting reactant by mole ratio: $\dfrac{Br_2}{limiting\ reactant}$

6
Mass of Br_2 in g
multiply by the molar mass of Br_2

5
Amount of Br_2 in mol

$$\underset{given}{g\ KBr} \times \frac{\overset{\frac{1}{molar\ mass\ KBr}}{1\ mol\ KBr}}{119.00\ g\ KBr} = mol\ KBr$$

$$\underset{given}{g\ Cl_2} \times \frac{\overset{\frac{1}{molar\ mass\ Cl_2}}{1\ mol\ Cl_2}}{70.90\ g\ Cl_2} = mol\ Cl_2$$

Choose one of the reactants, KBr for instance.

$$\underset{calculated\ above}{mol\ KBr} \times \frac{\overset{mole\ ratio}{1\ mol\ Cl_2}}{1\ mol\ KBr} = mol\ Cl_2\ needed$$

Determine the limiting reactant.

$$\underset{calculated\ above}{mol\ limiting\ reactant} \times \frac{\overset{mole\ ratio}{mol\ Br_2}}{mol\ limiting\ reactant} \times \frac{\overset{molar\ mass\ Br_2}{159.80\ g\ Br_2}}{1\ mol\ Br_2} = g\ Br_2$$

COMPUTE

$$3.205\ g\ \cancel{KBr} \times \frac{1\ mol\ KBr}{119.00\ g\ \cancel{KBr}} = 0.02693\ mol\ KBr$$

$$0.855\ g\ \cancel{Cl_2} \times \frac{1\ mol\ Cl_2}{70.90\ g\ \cancel{Cl_2}} = 0.0121\ mol\ Cl_2$$

Choose one of the reactants, KBr, for instance.

$$0.02693\ \cancel{mol\ KBr} \times \frac{1\ mol\ Cl_2}{2\ \cancel{mol\ KBr}} = 0.01346\ mol\ Cl_2\ needed$$

▌Problem Solving *continued*

Only 0.0121 mol Cl_2 is available. For all of the KBr to react, 0.0136 mol Cl_2 is needed. Therefore, Cl_2 is the limiting reactant.

$$0.0121 \text{ mol } Cl_2 \times \frac{1 \text{ mol } Br_2}{1 \text{ mol } Cl_2} \times \frac{159.80 \text{ g } Br_2}{1 \text{ mol } Br_2} = 1.93 \text{ g } Br_2$$

EVALUATE

Is the determination of limiting reactant reasonable?

Yes; the mass of 2 mol KBr is 238 g and the mass of 1 mol Cl_2 is about 71 g, so they react in roughly a 3:1 ratio by mass. 3.2 g KBr would require about 1 g of Cl_2, but only 0.855 g is available.

Are the units and significant figures of the mass of Br_2 correct?

The number of significant figures is correct because the mass of Cl_2 was given to three significant figures. Units cancel to give grams of Br_2.

Practice

1. A process by which zirconium metal can be produced from the mineral zirconium(IV) orthosilicate, $ZrSiO_4$, starts by reacting it with chlorine gas to form zirconium(IV) chloride.

$$ZrSiO_4 + 2Cl_2 \rightarrow ZrCl_4 + SiO_2 + O_2$$

What mass of $ZrCl_4$ can be produced if 862 g of $ZrSiO_4$ and 950. g of Cl_2 are available? You must first determine the limiting reactant. **ans: $ZrSiO_4$, 1.10 × 10^3 g $ZrCl_4$**

Additional Problems

1. Heating zinc sulfide in the presence of oxygen yields the following:

$$ZnS + O_2 \rightarrow ZnO + SO_2$$

If 1.72 mol of ZnS is heated in the presence of 3.04 mol of O_2, which reactant will be used up? Balance the equation first.

2. Use the following equation for the oxidation of aluminum in the following problems.

$$4Al + 3O_2 \rightarrow 2Al_2O_3$$

a. Which reactant is limiting if 0.32 mol Al and 0.26 mol O_2 are available?

b. How many moles of Al_2O_3 are formed from the reaction of 6.38×10^{-3} mol of O_2 and 9.15×10^{-3} mol of Al?

c. If 3.17 g of Al and 2.55 g of O_2 are available, which reactant is limiting?

3. In the production of copper from ore containing copper(II) sulfide, the ore is first roasted to change it to the oxide according to the following equation:

$$2CuS + 3O_2 \rightarrow 2CuO + 2SO_2$$

a. If 100 g of CuS and 56 g of O_2 are available, which reactant is limiting?

b. What mass of CuO can be formed from the reaction of 18.7 g of CuS and 12.0 g of O_2?

4. A reaction such as the one shown here is often used to demonstrate a single replacement reaction.

$$3CuSO_4(aq) + 2Fe(s) \rightarrow 3Cu(s) + Fe_2(SO_4)_3(aq)$$

If you place 0.092 mol of iron filings in a solution containing 0.158 mol of $CuSO_4$, what is the limiting reactant? How many moles of Cu will be formed?

5. In the reaction $BaCO_3 + 2HNO_3 \rightarrow Ba(NO_3)_2 + CO_2 + H_2O$, what mass of $Ba(NO_3)_2$ can be formed by combining 55 g $BaCO_3$ and 26 g HNO_3?

6. Bromine replaces iodine in magnesium iodide by the following process:

$$MgI_2 + Br_2 \rightarrow MgBr_2 + I_2$$

a. Which is the excess reactant when 560 g of MgI_2 and 360 g of Br_2 react, and what mass remains?

b. What mass of I_2 is formed in the same process?

7. Nickel replaces silver from silver nitrate in solution according to the following equation:

$$2AgNO_3 + Ni \rightarrow 2Ag + Ni(NO_3)_2$$

a. If you have 22.9 g of Ni and 112 g of $AgNO_3$, which reactant is in excess?

b. What mass of nickel(II) nitrate would be produced given the quantities above?

▌Problem Solving *continued*

8. Carbon disulfide, CS_2, is an important industrial substance. Its fumes can burn explosively in air to form sulfur dioxide and carbon dioxide.

$$CS_2(g) + O_2(g) \rightarrow SO_2(g) + CO_2(g)$$

If 1.60 mol of CS_2 burns with 5.60 mol of O_2, how many moles of the excess reactant will still be present when the reaction is over?

9. Although poisonous, mercury compounds were once used to kill bacteria in wounds and on the skin. One was called "ammoniated mercury" and is made from mercury(II) chloride according to the following equation:

$$HgCl_2(aq) + 2NH_3(aq) \rightarrow Hg(NH_2)Cl(s) + NH_4Cl(aq)$$

a. What mass of $Hg(NH_2)Cl$ could be produced from 0.91 g of $HgCl_2$ assuming plenty of ammonia is available?

b. What mass of $Hg(NH_2)Cl$ could be produced from 0.91 g of $HgCl_2$ and 0.15 g of NH_3 in solution?

10. Aluminum chips are sometimes added to sodium hydroxide-based drain cleaners because they react to generate hydrogen gas which bubbles and helps loosen material in the drain. The equation follows.

$$Al(s) + NaOH(aq) + H_2O(l) \rightarrow NaAlO_2(aq) + H_2(g)$$

a. Balance the equation.

b. How many moles of H_2 can be generated from 0.57 mol Al and 0.37 mol NaOH in excess water?

c. Which reactant should be limiting in order for the mixture to be most effective as a drain cleaner? Explain your choice.

11. Copper is changed to copper(II) ions by nitric acid according to the following equation:

$$4HNO_3 + Cu \rightarrow Cu(NO_3)_2 + 2NO_2 + 2H_2O$$

a. How many moles each of HNO_3 and Cu must react in order to produce 0.0845 mol of NO_2?

b. If 5.94 g of Cu and 23.23 g of HNO_3 are combined, which reactant is in excess?

12. One industrial process for producing nitric acid begins with the following reaction:

$$4NH_3 + 5O_2 \rightarrow 4NO + 6H_2O$$

a. If 2.90 mol NH_3 and 3.75 mol O_2 are available, how many moles of each product are formed?

b. Which reactant is limiting if 4.20×10^4 g of NH_3 and 1.31×10^5 g of O_2 are available?

c. What mass of NO is formed in the reaction of 869 kg of NH_3 and 2480 kg O_2?

| Problem Solving *continued*

13. Acetaldehyde CH_3CHO is manufactured by the reaction of ethanol with copper(II) oxide according to the following equation:

$$CH_3CH_2OH + CuO \rightarrow CH_3CHO + H_2O + Cu$$

What mass of acetaldehyde can be produced by the reaction between 620 g of ethanol and 1020 g of CuO? What mass of which reactant will be left over?

14. Hydrogen bromide can be produced by a reaction among bromine, sulfur dioxide, and water as follows.

$$SO_2 + Br_2 + H_2O \rightarrow 2HBr + H_2SO_4$$

If 250 g of SO_2 and 650 g of Br_2 react in the presence of excess water, what mass of HBr will be formed?

15. Sulfur dioxide can be produced in the laboratory by the reaction of hydrochloric acid and a sulfite salt such as sodium sulfite.

$$Na_2SO_3 + 2HCl \rightarrow 2NaCl + SO_2 + H_2O$$

What mass of SO_2 can be made from 25.0 g of Na_2SO_3 and 22.0 g of HCl?

16. The rare-earth metal terbium is produced from terbium(III) fluoride and calcium metal by the following displacement reaction:

$$2TbF_3 + 3Ca \rightarrow 3CaF_2 + 2Tb$$

a. Given 27.5 g of TbF_3 and 6.96 g of Ca, how many grams of terbium could be produced?

b. How many grams of the excess reactant are left over?

Skills Worksheet)

Problem Solving

Percentage Yield

Although we can write perfectly balanced equations to represent perfect reactions, the reactions themselves are often not perfect. A reaction does not always produce the quantity of products that the balanced equation seems to guarantee. This happens not because the equation is wrong but because reactions in the real world seldom produce perfect results.

As an example of an imperfect reaction, look again at the equation that shows the industrial production of ammonia.

$$N_2(g) + 3H_2(g) \rightarrow 2NH_3(g)$$

In the manufacture of ammonia, it is nearly impossible to produce 2 mol (34.08 g) of NH_3 from the simple reaction of 1 mol (28.02 g) of N_2 and 3 mol (6.06 g) of H_2 because some ammonia molecules begin breaking down into N_2 and H_2 molecules as soon as they are formed.

There are several reasons that real-world reactions do not produce products at a yield of 100%. Some are simple mechanical reasons, such as:

• Reactants or products leak out, especially when they are gases.
• The reactants are not 100% pure.
• Some product is lost when it is purified.

There are also many chemical reasons, including:

• The products decompose back into reactants (as with the ammonia process).
• The products react to form different substances.
• Some of the reactants react in ways other than the one shown in the equation. These are called *side reactions*.
• The reaction occurs very slowly. This is especially true of reactions involving organic substances.

Chemists are very concerned with the yields of reactions because they must find ways to carry out reactions economically and on a large scale. If the yield of a reaction is too small, the products may not be competitive in the marketplace. If a reaction has only a 50% yield, it produces only 50% of the amount of product that it theoretically should. In this chapter, you will learn how to solve problems involving real-world reactions and percentage yield.

Problem Solving *continued*

General Plan for Solving Percentage-Yield Problems

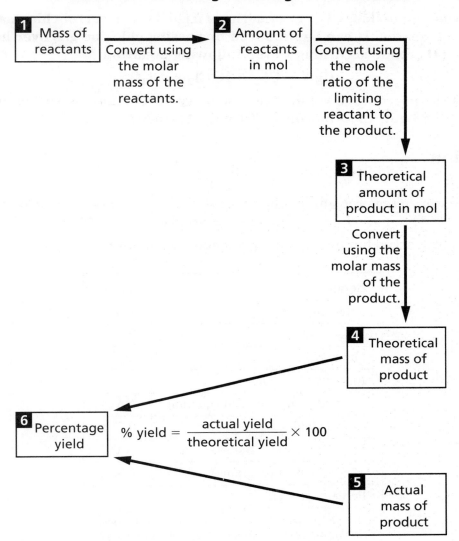

1 Mass of reactants

Convert using the molar mass of the reactants.

2 Amount of reactants in mol

Convert using the mole ratio of the limiting reactant to the product.

3 Theoretical amount of product in mol

Convert using the molar mass of the product.

4 Theoretical mass of product

6 Percentage yield

$$\% \text{ yield} = \frac{\text{actual yield}}{\text{theoretical yield}} \times 100$$

5 Actual mass of product

❚ Problem Solving *continued*

Sample Problem 1

Dichlorine monoxide, Cl_2O is sometimes used as a powerful chlorinating agent in research. It can be produced by passing chlorine gas over heated mercury(II) oxide according to the following equation:

$$HgO + Cl_2 \rightarrow HgCl_2 + Cl_2O$$

What is the percentage yield, if the quantity of reactants is sufficient to produce 0.86 g of Cl_2O but only 0.71 g is obtained?

Solution

ANALYZE

What is given in the problem? **the balanced equation, the actual yield of Cl_2O, and the theoretical yield of Cl_2O**

What are you asked to find? **the percentage yield of Cl_2O**

Items	Data
Substance	Cl_2O
Mass available	NA*
Molar mass	NA
Amount of reactant	NA
Coefficient in balanced equation	NA
Actual yield	0.71 g
Theoretical yield (moles)	NA
Theoretical yield (grams)	0.86 g
Percentage yield	?

*Although this table has many *Not Applicable* entries, you will need much of this information in other kinds of percentage-yield problems.

PLAN

What steps are needed to calculate the percentage yield of Cl_2O?
Compute the ratio of the actual yield to the theoretical yield, and multiply by 100 to convert to a percentage.

❙ Problem Solving *continued*

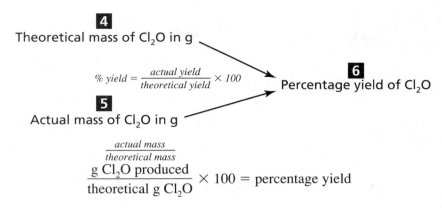

4 Theoretical mass of Cl_2O in g

$$\% \; yield = \frac{actual \; yield}{theoretical \; yield} \times 100$$

6 Percentage yield of Cl_2O

5 Actual mass of Cl_2O in g

$$\frac{\overset{\frac{actual \; mass}{theoretical \; mass}}{g \; Cl_2O \; produced}}{theoretical \; g \; Cl_2O} \times 100 = percentage \; yield$$

COMPUTE

$$\frac{0.71 \; g \; Cl_2O}{0.86 \; g \; Cl_2O} \times 100 = 83\% \; yield$$

EVALUATE

Are the units correct?
Yes; the ratio was converted to a percentage.

Is the number of significant figures correct?
Yes; the number of significant figures is correct because the data were given to two significant figures.

Is the answer reasonable?
Yes; 83% is about 5/6, which appears to be close to the ratio 0.71/0.86.

Practice

1. Calculate the percentage yield in each of the following cases:

a. theoretical yield is 50.0 g of product; actual yield is 41.9 g **ans: 83.8% yield**

b. theoretical yield is 290 kg of product; actual yield is 270 kg **ans: 93% yield**

▌Problem Solving *continued*

c. theoretical yield is 6.05×10^4 kg of product; actual yield is 4.18×10^4 kg
ans: 69.1% yield

d. theoretical yield is 0.00192 g of product; actual yield is 0.00089 g **ans: 46% yield**

Problem Solving *continued*

Sample Problem 2

Acetylene, C_2H_2, can be used as an industrial starting material for the production of many organic compounds. Sometimes, it is first brominated to form 1,1,2,2-tetrabromoethane, $CHBr_2CHBr_2$, which can then be reacted in many different ways to make other substances. The equation for the bromination of acetylene follows:

$$\underset{\textit{acetylene}}{C_2H_2} + 2Br_2 \rightarrow \underset{\textit{1,1,2,2-tetrabromoethane}}{CHBr_2CHBR_2}$$

If 72.0 g of C_2H_2 reacts with excess bromine and 729 g of the product is recovered, what is the percentage yield of the reaction?

Solution

ANALYZE

What is given in the problem? **the balanced equation, the mass of acetylene that reacts, and the mass of tetrabromoethane produced**

What are you asked to find? **the percentage yield of tetrabromoethane**

Items	Data	
Substance	C_2H_2	$CHBr_2CHBr_2$
Mass available	72.0 g available	NA
Molar mass*	26.04 g/mol	345.64 g/mol
Amount of reactant	?	NA
Coefficient in balanced equation	1	1
Actual yield	NA	729 g
Theoretical yield (moles)	NA	?
Theoretical yield (grams)	NA	?
Percentage yield	NA	?

*determined from the periodic table

PLAN

What steps are needed to calculate the theoretical yield of tetrabromoethane?
Set up a stoichiometry calculation to find the amount of product that can be formed from the given amount of reactant.

What steps are needed to calculate the percentage yield of tetrabromoethane?
Compute the ratio of the actual yield to the theoretical yield, and multiply by 100 to convert to a percentage.

| Problem Solving *continued*

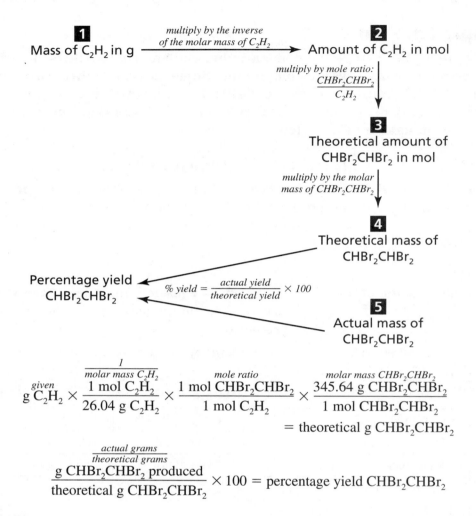

1
Mass of C_2H_2 in g $\xrightarrow{\text{multiply by the inverse}\atop\text{of the molar mass of } C_2H_2}$ **2** Amount of C_2H_2 in mol

multiply by mole ratio:
$$\frac{CHBr_2CHBr_2}{C_2H_2}$$

3
Theoretical amount of
$CHBr_2CHBr_2$ in mol

*multiply by the molar
mass of* $CHBr_2CHBr_2$

4
Theoretical mass of
$CHBr_2CHBr_2$

Percentage yield
$CHBr_2CHBr_2$ $\longleftarrow$ $\%\ yield = \frac{actual\ yield}{theoretical\ yield} \times 100$

5
Actual mass of
$CHBr_2CHBr_2$

$$\text{g} \overset{given}{C_2H_2} \times \overset{\frac{1}{molar\ mass\ C_2H_2}}{\frac{1\ \text{mol}\ C_2H_2}{26.04\ \text{g}\ C_2H_2}} \times \overset{mole\ ratio}{\frac{1\ \text{mol}\ CHBr_2CHBr_2}{1\ \text{mol}\ C_2H_2}} \times \overset{molar\ mass\ CHBr_2CHBr_2}{\frac{345.64\ \text{g}\ CHBr_2CHBr_2}{1\ \text{mol}\ CHBr_2CHBr_2}}$$
$$= \text{theoretical g } CHBr_2CHBr_2$$

$$\frac{\overset{actual\ grams}{\overset{theoretical\ grams}{}}}{\frac{\text{g } CHBr_2CHBr_2 \text{ produced}}{\text{theoretical g } CHBr_2CHBr_2}} \times 100 = \text{percentage yield } CHBr_2CHBr_2$$

COMPUTE

$$72.0\ \text{g}\ \cancel{C_2H_2} \times \frac{1\ \text{mol}\ \cancel{C_2H_2}}{26.04\ \text{g}\ \cancel{C_2H_2}} \times \frac{1\ \text{mol}\ \cancel{CHBr_2CHBr_2}}{1\ \text{mol}\ \cancel{C_2H_2}} \times \frac{345.64\ \text{g}\ CHBr_2CHBr_2}{1\ \text{mol}\ \cancel{CHBr_2CHBr_2}}$$
$$= 956\ \text{g}\ CHBr_2CHBr_2$$

$$\frac{729\ \text{g}\ CHBr_2CHBr_2}{956\ \text{g}\ CHBr_2CHBr_2} \times 100 = 76.3\%\ \text{yield}$$

EVALUATE

Are the units correct?

**Yes; units canceled to give grams of $CHBr_2CHBr_2$. Also, the ratio was converted
to a percentage.**

Is the number of significant figures correct?

**Yes; the number of significant figures is correct because the data were given to
three significant figures.**

Is the answer reasonable?

**Yes; about 3 mol of acetylene were used and the theoretical yield is the mass of
about 3 mol tetrabromoethane.**

| Problem Solving *continued*

Practice

1. In the commercial production of the element arsenic, arsenic(III) oxide is heated with carbon, which reduces the oxide to the metal according to the following equation:

$$2As_2O_3 + 3C \rightarrow 3CO_2 + 4As$$

a. If 8.87 g of As_2O_3 is used in the reaction and 5.33 g of As is produced, what is the percentage yield? **ans: 79.3% yield**

b. If 67 g of carbon is used up in a different reaction and 425 g of As is produced, calculate the percentage yield of this reaction. **ans: 76% yield**

| **Problem Solving** *continued*

Additional Problems

1. Ethyl acetate is a sweet-smelling solvent used in varnishes and fingernail-polish remover. It is produced industrially by heating acetic acid and ethanol together in the presence of sulfuric acid, which is added to speed up the reaction. The ethyl acetate is distilled off as it is formed. The equation for the process is as follows.

$$\underset{\text{acetic acid}}{CH_3COOH} + \underset{\text{ethanol}}{CH_3CH_2OH} \xrightarrow{H_2SO_4} \underset{\text{ethyl acetate}}{CH_3COOCH_2CH_3} + H_2O$$

Determine the percentage yield in the following cases:

a. 68.3 g of ethyl acetate should be produced but only 43.9 g is recovered.

b. 0.0419 mol of ethyl acetate is produced but 0.0722 mol is expected. (Hint: Percentage yield can also be calculated by dividing the actual yield in moles by the theoretical yield in moles.)

c. 4.29 mol of ethanol is reacted with excess acetic acid, but only 2.98 mol of ethyl acetate is produced.

d. A mixture of 0.58 mol ethanol and 0.82 mol acetic acid is reacted and 0.46 mol ethyl acetate is produced. (Hint: What is the limiting reactant?)

2. Assume the following hypothetical reaction takes place.

$$2A + 7B \rightarrow 4C + 3D$$

Calculate the percentage yield in each of the following cases:

a. The reaction of 0.0251 mol of A produces 0.0349 mol of C.

b. The reaction of 1.19 mol of A produces 1.41 mol of D.

c. The reaction of 189 mol of B produces 39 mol of D.

d. The reaction of 3500 mol of B produces 1700 mol of C.

3. Elemental phosphorus can be produced by heating calcium phosphate from rocks with silica sand (SiO_2) and carbon in the form of coke. The following reaction takes place.

$$Ca_3(PO_4)_2 + 3SiO_2 + 5C \rightarrow 3CaSiO_3 + 2P + 5CO$$

a. If 57 mol of $Ca_3(PO_4)_2$ is used and 101 mol of $CaSiO_3$ is obtained, what is the percentage yield?

b. Determine the percentage yield obtained if 1280 mol of carbon is consumed and 622 mol of $CaSiO_3$ is produced.

c. The engineer in charge of this process expects a yield of 81.5%. If 1.4×10^5 mol of $Ca_3(PO_4)_2$ is used, how many moles of phosphorus will be produced?

4. Tungsten (W) can be produced from its oxide by reacting the oxide with hydrogen at a high temperature according to the following equation:

$$WO_3 + 3H_2 \rightarrow W + 3H_2O$$

a. What is the percentage yield if 56.9 g of WO_3 yields 41.4 g of tungsten?

44

b. How many moles of tungsten will be produced from 3.72 g of WO_3 if the yield is 92.0%?

c. A chemist carries out this reaction and obtains 11.4 g of tungsten. If the percentage yield is 89.4%, what mass of WO_3 was used?

5. Carbon tetrachloride, CCl_4, is a solvent that was once used in large quantities in dry cleaning. Because it is a dense liquid that does not burn, it was also used in fire extinguishers. Unfortunately, its use was discontinued because it was found to be a carcinogen. It was manufactured by the following reaction:

$$CS_2 + 3Cl_2 \rightarrow CCl_4 + S_2Cl_2$$

The reaction was economical because the byproduct disulfur dichloride, S_2Cl_2, could be used by industry in the manufacture of rubber products and other materials.

a. What is the percentage yield of CCl_4 if 719 kg is produced from the reaction of 410. kg of CS_2.

b. If 67.5 g of Cl_2 are used in the reaction and 39.5 g of S_2Cl_2 is produced, what is the percentage yield?

c. If the percentage yield of the industrial process is 83.3%, how many kilograms of CS_2 should be reacted to obtain 5.00×10^4 kg of CCl_4? How many kilograms of S_2Cl_2 will be produced, assuming the same yield for that product?

6. Nitrogen dioxide, NO_2, can be converted to dinitrogen pentoxide, N_2O_5, by reacting it with ozone, O_3. The reaction of NO_2 takes place according to the following equation:

$$2NO_2(g) + O_3(g) \rightarrow N_2O_5(s \text{ or } g) + O_2(g)$$

a. Calculate the percentage yield for a reaction in which 0.38 g of NO_2 reacts and 0.36 g of N_2O_5 is recovered.

b. What mass of N_2O_5 will result from the reaction of 6.0 mol of NO_2 if there is a 61.1% yield in the reaction?

7. In the past, hydrogen chloride, HCl, was made using the *salt-cake* method as shown in the following equation:

$$2NaCl(s) + H_2SO_4(aq) \rightarrow Na_2SO_4(s) + 2HCl(g)$$

If 30.0 g of NaCl and 0.250 mol of H_2SO_4 are available, and 14.6 g of HCl is made, what is the percentage yield?

8. Cyanide compounds such as sodium cyanide, NaCN, are especially useful in gold refining because they will react with gold to form a stable compound that can then be separated and broken down to retrieve the gold. Ore containing only small quantities of gold can be used in this form of "chemical mining." The equation for the reaction follows.

$$4Au + 8NaCN + 2H_2O + O_2 \rightarrow 4NaAu(CN)_2 + 4NaOH$$

a. What percentage yield is obtained if 410 g of gold produces 540 g of $NaAu(CN)_2$?

❚ Problem Solving *continued*

b. Assuming a 79.6% yield in the conversion of gold to $NaAu(CN)_2$, what mass of gold would produce 1.00 kg of $NaAu(CN)_2$?

c. Given the conditions in (b), what mass of gold ore that is 0.001% gold would be needed to produce 1.00 kg of $NaAu(CN)_2$?

9. Diiodine pentoxide is useful in devices such as respirators because it reacts with the dangerous gas carbon monoxide, CO, to produce relatively harmless CO_2 according to the following equation:

$$I_2O_5 + 5CO \rightarrow I_2 + 5CO_2$$

a. In testing a respirator, 2.00 g of carbon monoxide gas is passed through diiodine pentoxide. Upon analyzing the results, it is found that 3.17 g of I_2 was produced. Calculate the percentage yield of the reaction.

b. Assuming that the yield in (a) resulted because some of the CO did not react, calculate the mass of CO that passed through.

10. Sodium hypochlorite, NaClO, the main ingredient in household bleach, is produced by bubbling chlorine gas through a strong lye (sodium hydroxide, NaOH) solution. The following equation shows the reaction that occurs.

$$2NaOH(aq) + Cl_2(g) \rightarrow NaCl(aq) + NaClO(aq) + H_2O(l)$$

a. What is the percentage yield of the reaction if 1.2 kg of Cl_2 reacts to form 0.90 kg of NaClO?

b. If a plant operator wants to make 25 metric tons of NaClO per day at a yield of 91.8%, how many metric tons of chlorine gas must be on hand each day?

c. What mass of NaCl is formed per mole of chlorine gas at a yield of 81.8%?

d. At what rate in kg per hour must NaOH be replenished if the reaction produces 370 kg/h of NaClO at a yield of 79.5%? Assume that all of the NaOH reacts to produce this yield.

11. Magnesium burns in oxygen to form magnesium oxide. However, when magnesium burns in air, which is only about 1/5 oxygen, side reactions form other products, such as magnesium nitride, Mg_3N_2.

a. Write a balanced equation for the burning of magnesium in oxygen.

b. If enough magnesium burns in air to produce 2.04 g of magnesium oxide but only 1.79 g is obtained, what is the percentage yield?

c. Magnesium will react with pure nitrogen to form the nitride, Mg_3N_2. Write a balanced equation for this reaction.

d. If 0.097 mol of Mg react with nitrogen and 0.027 mol of Mg_3N_2 is produced, what is the percentage yield of the reaction?

Problem Solving *continued*

12. Some alcohols can be converted to organic acids by using sodium dichromate and sulfuric acid. The following equation shows the reaction of 1-propanol to propanoic acid.

$$3CH_3CH_2CH_2OH + 2Na_2Cr_2O_7 + 8H_2SO_4 \rightarrow$$
$$3CH_3CH_2COOH + 2Cr_2(SO_4)_3 + 2Na_2SO_4 + 11H_2O$$

a. If 0.89 g of 1-propanol reacts and 0.88 g of propanoic acid is produced, what is the percentage yield?

b. A chemist uses this reaction to obtain 1.50 mol of propanoic acid. The reaction consumes 136 g of propanol. Calculate the percentage yield.

c. Some 1-propanol of uncertain purity is used in the reaction. If 116 g of $Na_2Cr_2O_7$ are consumed in the reaction and 28.1 g of propanoic acid are produced, what is the percentage yield?

13. Acrylonitrile, $C_3H_3N(g)$, is an important ingredient in the production of various fibers and plastics. Acrylonitrile is produced from the following reaction:

$$C_3H_6(g) + NH_3(g) + O_2(g) \rightarrow C_3H_3N(g) + H_2O(g)$$

If 850. g of C_3H_6 is mixed with 300. g of NH_3 and unlimited O_2, to produce 850. g of acrylonitrile, what is the percentage yield? You must first balance the equation.

14. Methanol, CH_3OH, is frequently used in race cars as fuel. It is produced as the sole product of the combination of carbon monoxide gas and hydrogen gas.

a. If 430. kg of hydrogen react, what mass of methanol could be produced?

b. If 3.12×10^3 kg of methanol are actually produced, what is the percentage yield?

15. The compound, $C_6H_{16}N_2$, is one of the starting materials in the production of nylon. It can be prepared from the following reaction involving adipic acid, $C_6H_{10}O_4$:

$$C_6H_{10}O_4(l) + 2NH_3(g) + 4H_2(g) \rightarrow C_6H_{16}N_2(l) + 4H_2O(l)$$

What is the percentage yield if 750. g of adipic acid results in the production of 578 g of $C_6H_{16}N_2$?

16. Plants convert carbon dioxide to oxygen during photosynthesis according to the following equation:

$$CO_2 + H_2O \rightarrow C_6H_{12}O_6 + O_2$$

Balance this equation, and calculate how much oxygen would be produced if 1.37×10^4 g of carbon dioxide reacts with a percentage yield of 63.4%.

17. Lime, CaO, is frequently added to streams and lakes which have been polluted by acid rain. The calcium oxide reacts with the water to form a base that can neutralize the acid as shown in the following reaction:

$$CaO(s) + H_2O(l) \rightarrow Ca(OH)_2(s)$$

If 2.67×10^2 mol of base are needed to neutralize the acid in a lake, and the above reaction has a percentage yield of 54.3%, what is the mass, in kilograms, of lime that must be added to the lake?

Assessment

Quiz

Section: Calculating Quantities in Reactions

In the space provided, write the letter of the term or phrase that best answers the question.

_____ **1.** The chemical equation $P_4O_{10} + 6H_2O \rightarrow 4H_3PO_4$ can be correctly interpreted as
   a. 1 molecule of P_4O_{10} + 6 molecules of H_2O form 4 molecules of H_3PO4.
   b. 1 mol P_4O_{10} + 6 mol H_2O reacts to form 4 mol H_3PO_4.
   c. 1 g P_4O_{10} + 6 g H_2O produces 4 g H_3PO_4.
   d. Both (a) and (b)

_____ **2.** Stoichiometry is the branch of chemistry that deals with the _____ between elements and compounds as reactants and products in a chemical reaction.
   a. bonding
   b. energy transfers
   c. numerical relationship
   d. physical interactions

_____ **3.** How many mole ratios can be correctly obtained from the following chemical equation?
$$Na_2S + Cd(NO_3)_2 \rightarrow 2NaNO_3 + CdS$$
   a. 1
   b. 4
   c. 12
   d. 16

_____ **4.** Molar mass can be used to relate
   a. mass of reactant to moles of reactant.
   b. moles of product to mass of product.
   c. mass of product to moles of product.
   d. All of the above

_____ **5.** In the chemical reaction described by the equation
$$4Fe(s) + 3O_2(g) \rightarrow 2Fe_2O_3(s),$$
the mole ratio of iron(III) oxide to iron is
   a. 1:1.
   b. 1:2.
   c. 2:3.
   d. 4:1.

Quiz *continued*

_____ **6.** The expression mass $\times \dfrac{1}{\text{molar mass}}$ has the unit

     a. mol^2/g.
     b. g/mol^2.
     c. mol.
     d. g.

_____ **7.** In the chemical equation $wA + xB \rightarrow yC + zD$, if one knows the mass of A and the molar masses of A, B, C, and D, one can determine
     a. the mass of each reactant and product.
     b. the mass of B only.
     c. the total mass of C and D only.
     d. the total mass of A and B only.

_____ **8.** The expression volume $\times \dfrac{1}{\text{molar volume}}$ has the unit

     a. g/L.   **c.** mol.
     b. L.   **d.** mol/L.

_____ **9.** What could you use to calculate the volume of ammonia gas produced by the reaction of 2.0 L of nitrogen gas in excess hydrogen gas at non-STP conditions according to the chemical equation below?

$$N_2(g) + 3H_2(g) \rightarrow 2NH_3(g)$$

     a. one density, one molar mass, and one mole ratio.
     b. one density, two molar masses, and one mole ratio.
     c. two densities, two molar masses, and one mole ratio.
     d. two densities, two molar masses, and two mole ratios.

_____ **10.** If, in the reaction $C_5H_{12}(l) \rightarrow C_5H_8(l) + 2H_2(g)$, 1.50×10^{22} molecules of C_5H_{12} decompose, then the following expression

$$1.50 \times 10^{22} \text{ molecules } C_5H_{12} \times \dfrac{1 \text{ mol } C_5H_{12}}{6.022 \times 10^{23} \text{ molecules } C_5H_{12}} \times$$

$$\dfrac{2 \text{ mol } H_2}{1 \text{ mol } C_5H_{12}} \times \dfrac{2.02 \text{ g } H_2}{1 \text{ mol } H_2}$$

calculates the _____ of H_2 molecules produced.
     a. number   **c.** mass
     b. moles   **d.** volume

Assessment

Quiz

Section: Limiting Reactants and Percentage Yield

In the space provided, write the letter of the term or phrase that best answers the question.

_____ **1.** If, in the reaction $A + B \rightarrow C + D$, the quantity of B is insufficient to react with all of A,
  a. A is the limiting reactant.
  b. B is the limiting reactant.
  c. Both (a) and (b)
  d. Neither (a) nor (b)

_____ **2.** If, in the reaction $A + B \rightarrow C + D$, the quantity of B is insufficient to react with all of A,
  a. the reaction rate increases.
  b. excess product forms.
  c. C and D react.
  d. the reaction stops.

For items 3–5, use the following reaction, which is used commercially to produce elemental arsenic by heating arsenic(III) oxide with carbon.

$$2As_2O_3 + 3C \rightarrow 3CO_2 + 4As$$

_____ **3.** If 6.0 mol of each reactant are available for the above reaction, the mixture remaining after the reaction should contain
  a. 4.0 mol As_2O_3.
  b. 3.0 mol C.
  c. 2.0 mol As_2O_3.
  d. no reactants.

_____ **4.** If 6.0 mol of each reactant are available for the above reaction, the mixture remaining after the reaction should contain
  a. 7.5 mol As.
  b. 6.7 mol As.
  c. 6.0 mol CO_2.
  d. equal quantities of the products.

_____ **5.** If 8.0 mol As_2O_3 is reacted with excess carbon, the theoretical yield of the above reaction is
  a. 32 mol As.
  b. 16 mol As.
  c. 8 mol As.
  d. 4 mol As.

Quiz *continued*

_____ **6.** The measured amount of product obtained from a chemical reaction is the
   a. percentage yield.
   b. theoretical yield.
   c. actual yield.
   d. mole ratio.

_____ **7.** Can the combustion of 1.0 mole of methane, CH_4, given by the equation $CH_4 + 2O_2 \rightarrow 2H_2O + CO_2$, have an actual yield of 1.0 mol CO_2?
   a. No
   b. Yes
   c. Yes, only if oxygen is the limiting reactant
   d. Yes, only if the water is removed

_____ **8.** Actual yield is affected by
   a. side reactions that compete with the main reactions.
   b. reverse reactions that cause products to reform reactants.
   c. amounts of reactants.
   d. All of the above

_____ **9.** If the percentage yield of I_2 is 80% for the following reaction, $I_2O_5 + 5CO \rightarrow I_2 + 5CO_2$, then
   a. 20% of the reactants remain.
   b. the percentage yield of CO_2 is 80%.
   c. Both (a) and (b)
   d. Neither (a) nor (b)

_____ **10.** What is the correct mathematical expression for the relationship among percentage yield, actual yield, and theoretical yield?
   a. actual yield $= \dfrac{\text{percentage yield}}{\text{theoretical yield}} \times 100$

   b. percentage yield $= \dfrac{\text{actual yield}}{\text{theoretical yield}} \times 100$

   c. percentage yield $= \dfrac{\text{theoretical yield}}{\text{actual yield}} \times 100$

   d. theoretical yield $= \dfrac{\text{actual yield}}{\text{percentage yield}} \times 100$

Assessment

Quiz

Section: Stoichiometry and Cars

In the space provided, write the letter of the term or phrase that best answers the question.

_____ 1. The function of an automobile air bag during a collision is to
  a. increase the braking force of the car.
  b. slow the forward motion of the passenger.
  c. retard fire.
  d. prevent the car doors from opening.

_____ 2. Air bags must inflate _____ after impact.
  a. 10^{-6} s
  b. 10^{-3} s
  c. 10^{-1} s
  d. 1.0 s

_____ 3. When an automobile safety air bag is inflated, it contains mostly
  a. air.
  b. $CO_2(g)$.
  c. $N_2(g)$.
  d. $O_2(g)$.

_____ 4. The following equation describes the second reaction that takes place in an airbag.

$$6Na(s) + Fe_2O_3(s) \rightarrow 3Na_2O(s) + 2Fe(s) + \text{energy}$$

The function of iron(III) oxide, Fe_2O_3, in this reaction is to
  a. produce more gas.
  b. cool the gas produced in the first reaction.
  c. combine with the very reactive element sodium.
  d. Both (b) and (c)

_____ 5. What is the mole ratio of fuel to oxygen for the combustion of isooctane described by the following chemical equation?

$$2C_8H_{18}(g) + 25O_2(g) \rightarrow 16CO_2(g) + 18H_2O(g)$$

  a. 1:8
  b. 1:9
  c. 2:25
  d. 25:16

Quiz *continued*

_____ **6.** The limiting reactant in the combustion of fuel in a car is
    a. the fuel.
    b. CO_2.
    c. O_2.
    d. Both (a) and (c)

_____ **7.** The greatest fuel-to-oxygen ratio should occurs when a car's engine is
    a. idling.
    b. running at normal speeds.
    c. starting.
    d. stopping.

_____ **8.** The function of a carburetor in a small internal-combustion engine is to
    a. mix fuel and oxygen.
    b. produce power.
    c. convert chemical energy to kinetic energy.
    d. prevent combustion.

_____ **9.** Catalytic converters
    a. use phosphorus as a catalyst.
    b. increase the decomposition rates of oxides of nitrogen.
    c. work more efficiently with leaded gasoline.
    d. operate best for exhaust gases at low temperatures.

_____ **10.** Ozone, O_3, is produced by the following reaction:

$$NO_2(g) + O_2(g) \rightarrow NO(g) + O_3(g)$$

What mass of ozone will form from the reaction of 2.0 g NO_2 in a car's exhaust and excess oxygen?
    a. 3.3 g O_3
    b. 2.0 g O_3
    c. 1.5 g O_3
    d. cannot be predicted

Assessment

Chapter Test

Stoichiometry

In the space provided, write the letter of the term or phrase that best completes each statement or best answers each question.

_____ 1. For the reaction $SO_3 + H_2O \rightarrow H_2SO_4$, calculate the percentage yield if 500. g of sulfur trioxide react with excess water to produce 575 g of sulfuric acid.
    a. 82.7%
    b. 88.3%
    c. 91.2%
    d. 93.9%

_____ 2. In the reaction $2Al_2O_3 \rightarrow 4Al + 3O_2$, what is the mole ratio of aluminum to oxygen?
    a. 10:6
    b. 3:4
    c. 2:3
    d. 4:3

_____ 3. Fewer steps are required to solve stoichiometry problems when the reactant is given in
    a. grams and the product is sought in grams.
    b. moles and the product is sought in moles.
    c. grams and the product is sought in liters.
    d. liters and the product is sought in number of atoms.

_____ 4. Which of the following mathematical expressions correctly states the relationship among percentage yield, actual yield, and theoretical yield?

    i. $\text{actual yield} = \dfrac{\text{percentage yield}}{\text{theoretical yield}} \times 100$

    ii. $\text{percentage yield} = \dfrac{\text{actual yield}}{\text{theoretical yield}} \times 100$

    iii. $\text{theoretical yield} = \dfrac{\text{actual yield}}{\text{percentage yield}} \times 100$

    a. i
    b. ii
    c. iii
    d. Both (b) and (c)

_____ **5.** The participation of other reactants in a chemical reaction is restricted by the
   a. limiting reactant.
   b. limiting product.
   c. excess reactant.
   d. excess product.

_____ **6.** Which of the following expressions is *not* a legitimate conversion factor?
   a. $\dfrac{1 \text{ mol}}{6.022 \times 10^{23} \text{ atoms}}$
   b. $\dfrac{28.02 \text{ g N}_2}{1 \text{ mol N}_2}$
   c. $\dfrac{1 \text{ g C}}{6.022 \times 10^{23} \text{ atoms C}}$
   d. $\dfrac{2.02 \text{ g H}_2}{1 \text{ mol H}_2}$

_____ **7.** For the reaction $P_4(s) + 5O_2(g) \rightarrow P_4O_{10}(s)$, if 3 mol of phosphorus react with 10 mol of oxygen, the theoretical yield of phosphorus(V) oxide will be
   a. 1 mol.
   b. 2 mol.
   c. 3 mol.
   d. 10 mol.

_____ **8.** When a chemical reaction is performed in industry, the ____ chemical is often chosen as the excess reagent.
   a. least expensive and most abundant
   b. most expensive and least abundant
   c. least expensive and least abundant
   d. most expensive and most abundant

_____ **9.** A convenient stoichiometric measurement for an evolving gas is
   a. volume.
   b. mass.
   c. atoms.
   d. molecules.

_____ **10.** Percent yield represents the ____ of a chemical reaction.
   a. efficiency
   b. speed
   c. individual steps
   d. rate

_____11. The pollution produced by combustion engines can be partially controlled by which of the following?
   a. the use of a catalytic converter
   b. adjusting the contents of the gasoline
   c. having a well-tuned engine
   d. All of the above

_____12. The limiting reactant of a reaction can be used to calculate the
   a. actual yield.
   b. theoretical yield.
   c. experimental yield.
   d. Both (a) and (c)

_____13. The excess reactant when starting a gasoline (isooctane) engine is
   a. C_8H_{18}.
   b. CO_2.
   c. O_2.
   d. H_2O.

_____14. Which of the following factors does *not* affect the actual yield of a reaction?
   a. side reactions that compete with the main reaction
   b. reactions that are the reverse of the main reaction
   c. a mixture of reactants and products
   d. particles no longer reacting with each other

_____15. If the percentage yield for a chemical reaction is 80.0%, the
   a. actual yield is 80.0 g for every theoretical yield of 100. g.
   b. theoretical yield is 80.0 g for every actual yield of 100. g.
   c. actual yield is 80 times as much as the theoretical yield.
   d. theoretical yield is 80 times as much as the actual yield.

_____16. In the reaction, $CH_4(g) + 2O_2(g) \rightarrow CO_2(g) + 2H_2O(g)$, a mass of 125 g CH_4 is reacted with excess oxygen. The following expression

$$125 \text{ g } CH_4 \times \frac{1 \text{ mol } CH_4}{16.05 \text{ g } CH_4} \times \frac{2 \text{ mol } H_2O}{1 \text{ mol } CH_4} \times \frac{18.02 \text{ g } H_2O}{1 \text{ mol } H_2O}$$

calculates the
   a. mass of oxygen reacted.
   b. mass of carbon dioxide produced.
   c. mass of water produced.
   d. None of the above

_____ **17.** How many mole ratios can be correctly obtained from the following chemical equation?

$$P_4O_{10} + 6H_2O \rightarrow 4H_3PO_4$$

    a. 1
    b. 3
    c. 6
    d. 9

_____ **18.** In most chemical reactions, the amount of product obtained is
    a. equal to the theoretical yield.
    b. less than the theoretical yield.
    c. more than the theoretical yield.
    d. more than the percentage yield.

_____ **19.** The expression mass $\times \dfrac{1}{\text{molar mass}}$ has the unit
    a. g/mol.
    b. mol/g.
    c. g.
    d. mol.

_____ **20.** In the formation of silicon carbide, given by the chemical equation, $SiO_2(s) + 3C(s) \rightarrow SiC(s) + 2CO(g)$, 8 mol of each reactant are available for the reaction. What substance is the excess reactant?
    a. $SiO_2(s)$
    b. $C(s)$
    c. $SiC(s)$
    d. $CO(g)$

Chapter Test *continued*

Answer the following items in the spaces provided.

21. Explain why the limiting reactant may not be used completely when the percentage yield for a reaction is 70%.

_____

_____

_____

_____

_____

_____

22. Why should you use moles in stoichiometric problems?

_____

_____

_____

_____

23. The equation for the burning of gasoline shows that carbon dioxide, water, and energy are the only products of combustion. Yet burning gasoline in car engines causes air pollution. What information not revealed by the equation accounts for the pollutants?

_____

_____

_____

_____

_____

_____

_____

_____

Answer each of the following problems in the spaces provided.

24. What mass in grams of potassium chloride is produced if 100. g of potassium chlorate decompose according to the following equation?

$$2KClO_3(s) \xrightarrow{\text{heat}} 2KCl(s) + 3O_2(g)$$

25. A research chemist designing an air bag is looking at carbon dioxide as a possible gas for bag inflation. One of the reactions the chemist is working with is the following.

$$MgCO_3(s) \rightarrow MgO(s) + CO_2(g)$$

How many grams of magnesium carbonate are needed to produce enough carbon dioxide to inflate an air bag to a volume of 65.0 L? Use 1.961 g/L as the density of carbon dioxide gas.

Skills Practice Lab)   **DATASHEETS FOR IN-TEXT LAB**

Stoichiometry and Gravimetric Analysis

You are working for a company that makes water-softening agents for homes with hard water. Recently, there was a mix-up on the factory floor, and sodium carbonate solution was mistakenly mixed in a vat with an unknown quantity of distilled water. You must determine the amount of Na_2CO_3 in the vat in order to properly predict the percentage yield of the water-softening product.

When chemists are faced with problems that require them to determine the quantity of a substance by mass, they often use a technique called gravimetric analysis. In this technique, a small sample of the material undergoes a reaction with an excess of another reactant. The chosen reaction is one that almost always provides a yield near 100%. In other words, all of the reactant of unknown amount will be converted into product. If the mass of the product is carefully measured, you can use stoichiometry calculations to determine how much of the reactant of unknown amount was involved in the reaction. Then by comparing the size of the analysis sample with the size of the original material, you can determine exactly how much of the substance is present.

This procedure involves a double-displacement reaction between strontium chloride, $SrCl_2$, and sodium carbonate, Na_2CO_3. In general, this reaction can be used to determine the amount of any carbonate compound in a solution.

Remember that accurate results depend on precise mass measurements. Keep all glassware very clean, and do not lose any reactants or products during your lab work.

You will react an unknown amount of sodium carbonate with an excess of strontium chloride. After purifying the product, you will determine the following:

- how much product is present
- how much Na_2CO_3 must have been present to produce that amount of product,
- how much Na_2CO_3 is contained in the 575 L of solution

OBJECTIVES

Observe the reaction between strontium chloride and sodium carbonate, and write a balanced equation for the reaction.

Demonstrate proficiency with gravimetric methods.

Measure the mass of insoluble precipitate formed.

Draw conclusions and relate the mass of precipitate formed to the mass of reactants before the reaction.

Calculate the mass of sodium carbonate in a solution of unknown concentration.

Stoichiometry and Gravimetric Analysis *continued*

MATERIALS

- balance
- beaker tongs
- beakers, 250 mL (3)
- distilled water
- drying oven
- filter paper
- glass funnel or Büchner funnel
- glass stirring rod

- graduated cylinder, 100 mL
- Na_2CO_3 solution
- ring and ring stand
- rubber policeman
- spatula
- $SrCl_2$ solution, 0.30 M
- water bottle

Always wear safety goggles and a lab apron to protect your eyes and clothing. If you get a chemical in your eyes, immediately flush the chemical out at the eyewash station while calling to your teacher. Know the location of the emergency lab shower and eyewash station and the procedures for using them.

Do not touch any chemicals. If you get a chemical on your skin or clothing, wash the chemical off at the sink while calling to your teacher. Make sure you carefully read the labels and follow the precautions on all containers of chemicals that you use. If there are no precautions stated on the label, ask your teacher what precautions to follow. Do not taste any chemicals or items used in the laboratory. Never return leftovers to their original container; take only small amounts to avoid wasting supplies.

Do not heat glassware that is broken, chipped, or cracked. Use tongs or a hot mitt to handle heated glassware and other equipment because hot glassware does not always look hot.

Procedure

1. Put on safety goggles and lab apron.

2. Clean all of the necessary lab equipment with soap and water. Rinse each piece of equipment with distilled water.

3. Measure the mass of a piece of filter paper to the nearest 0.01 g, and record this value in your data table.

4. Set up a filtering apparatus, either a Büchner funnel or a gravity filtration, depending on what equipment is available.

5. Label a paper towel with your name, your class, and the date. Place the towel in a clean, dry 250 mL beaker, and measure and record the mass of the towel and beaker to the nearest 0.01 g.

6. Measure about 15 mL of the Na_2CO_3 solution into the graduated cylinder. Record this volume to the nearest 0.5 mL in your data table. Pour the Na_2CO_3 solution into a clean, empty 250 mL beaker. Carefully wash the graduated cylinder, and rinse it with distilled water.

7. Measure about 25 mL of the 0.30 M $SrCl_2$ solution into the graduated cylinder. Record this volume to the nearest 0.5 mL in your data table. Pour the $SrCl_2$ solution into the beaker with the Na_2CO_3 solution. Gently stir the solution and precipitate with a glass stirring rod.

8. Carefully measure another 10 mL of $SrCl_2$ into the graduated cylinder. Record the volume to the nearest 0.5 mL in your data table. Slowly add it to the beaker. Repeat this step until no more precipitate forms.

9. Once the precipitate has settled, slowly pour the mixture into the funnel. Be careful not to overfill the funnel because some of the precipitate could be lost between the filter paper and the funnel. Use the rubber policeman to transfer as much of the precipitate into the funnel as possible.

10. Rinse the rubber policeman into the beaker with a small amount of distilled water, and pour this solution into the funnel. Rinse the beaker several more times with small amounts of distilled water. Pour the rinse water into the funnel each time.

11. After all of the solution and rinses have drained through the funnel, slowly rinse the precipitate on the filter paper in the funnel with distilled water to remove any soluble impurities.

12. Carefully remove the filter paper from the funnel, and place it on the paper towel that you have labeled with your name. Unfold the filter paper, and place the paper towel, filter paper, and precipitate in the rinsed beaker. Then place the beaker in the drying oven. For best results, allow the precipitate to dry overnight.

13. Using beaker tongs, remove your sample from the drying oven, and allow it to cool. Measure and record the mass of the beaker with paper towel, filter paper, and precipitate to the nearest 0.01 g.

14. Dispose of the precipitate in a designated waste container. Pour the filtrate in the other 250 mL beaker into the designated waste container. Clean up the lab and all equipment after use, and dispose of substances according to your teacher's instructions. Wash your hands thoroughly after all lab work is finished and before you leave the lab.

Stoichiometry and Gravimetric Analysis *continued*

TABLE 1 GRAVIMETRIC ANALYSIS DATA

Volume of Na_2CO_3 solution added	
Volume of $SrCl_2$ solution added	
Mass of dry filter paper	
Mass of beaker with paper towel	
Mass of beaker with paper towel, filter paper, and precipitate	
Mass of precipitate	

Analysis

1. **Organizing Data** Write a balanced equation for the reaction. What is the precipitate? Write its empirical formula. (Hint: It was a double-displacement reaction.)

   _____

   _____

   _____

2. **Examining Data** Calculate the mass of the dry precipitate. Calculate the number of moles of precipitate produced in the reaction. (Hint: Use the results from step 13.)

3. **Examining Data** How many moles of Na_2CO_3 were present in the 15 mL sample?

Stoichiometry and Gravimetric Analysis *continued*

Conclusions

4. **Evaluating Methods** There was 0.30 mol of $SrCl_2$ in every liter of solution. Calculate the number of moles of $SrCl_2$ that were added. Determine whether $SrCl_2$ or Na_2CO_3 was the limiting reactant. Would this experiment have worked if the other reactant had been chosen as the limiting reactant? Explain why or why not.

_____

_____

_____

_____

_____

_____

5. **Evaluating Methods** Why was the precipitate rinsed in step 11? What soluble impurities could have been on the filter paper along with the precipitate? How would the calculated results vary if the precipitate had not been completely dry? Explain your answer.

_____

_____

_____

6. **Applying Conclusions** How many grams of Na_2CO_3 were present in the 15 mL sample?

7. **Applying Conclusions** How many grams of Na_2CO_3 are present in the 575 L? (Hint: Create a conversion factor to convert from the sample, with a volume of 15 mL, to the entire solution, with a volume of 575 L.)

8. Evaluating Methods Ask your teacher for the theoretical mass of Na_2CO_3 in the sample, and calculate your percentage error.

Extensions

1. **Designing Experiments** What possible sources of error can you identify with your procedure? If you can think of ways to eliminate them, ask your teacher to approve your plan, and run the procedure again.

_____

_____

_____

Gravimetric Analysis–Hard-Water Testing

March 3, 2004

George Taylor, Director of Analysis
CheMystery Labs, Inc.
52 Fulton Street
Springfield, VA 22150

Dear Mr. Taylor:

The city's Public Works Department is investigating new sources of water. One proposal involves drilling wells into a nearby aquifer that is protected from brackish water by a unique geological formation. Unfortunately, this formation is made of calcium minerals. If the concentration of calcium ions in the water is too high, the water will be "hard," and treating it to meet local water standards would be too expensive for us.

Water containing more than 120 mg of calcium per liter is considered hard. I have enclosed a sample of water that has been distilled from 1.0 L to its present volume. Please determine whether the water is of suitable quality.

We are seeking a firm to be our consultant for the entire testing process. Interested firms will be evaluated based on this water analysis. We look forward to receiving your report.

Sincerely,

Dana Rubio
City Manager

References

Review the Stoichiometry chapter for information about mass–mass stoichiometry. In this investigation, you will use a double-displacement reaction. Na_2CO_3 will be used as a reagent to identify how much calcium is present in a sample. Like strontium and other Group 2 metals, calcium salts react with carbonate-containing salts to produce an insoluble precipitate.

CheMystery Labs, Inc.
52 Fulton Street
Springfield, VA 22150

Memorandum

Date: March 4, 2004

To: Shane Thompson

From: George Taylor

We can solve the city's problem by doing some careful gravimetric analysis, because calcium salts and carbonate compounds undergo double-displacement reactions to yield insoluble calcium carbonate as a precipitate.

Before you begin your work, I will need the following information from you so that I can create our bid:

- a detailed one-page summary of your plan for the procedure, as well as all necessary data tables,

- a description of necessary calculations, and

- an itemized list of equipment.

After you complete the analysis, prepare a two-page report for Dana Rubio. Make sure to include the following items:

- a calculation of calcium concentration in mg/L for the water from the aquifer,

- an explanation of how you determined the amount of calcium in the sample, including measurements and calculations,

- a balanced chemical equation for the reaction, and

- explanations and estimations for any possible sources of error.

Always wear safety goggles and a lab apron to protect your eyes and clothing. If you get a chemical in your eyes, immediately flush the chemical out at the eyewash station while calling to your teacher. Know the location of the emergency lab shower and eyewash station and the procedures for using them.

Do not touch any chemicals. If you get a chemical on your skin or clothing, wash the chemical off at the sink while calling to your teacher. Make sure you carefully read the labels and follow the precautions on all containers of chemicals that you use. If there are no precautions stated on the label, ask your teacher what precautions to follow. Do not taste any chemicals or items used in the laboratory. Never return leftovers to their original container; take only small amounts to avoid wasting supplies.

Do not heat glassware that is broken, chipped, or cracked. Use tongs or a hot mitt to handle heated glassware and other equipment because hot glassware does not always look hot.

When using a Bunsen burner, confine long hair and loose clothing. If your clothing catches on fire, WALK to the emergency lab shower and use it to put out the fire.

Lesson Plan

Section: Calculating Quantities in Reactions

Pacing

Regular Schedule   **with lab(s):** NA   **without lab(s):** 3 days
Block Schedule   **with lab(s):** NA   **without lab(s):** 1½ days

Objectives

1. Use proportional reasoning to determine mole ratios from a balanced chemical equation.

2. Explain why mole ratios are central to solving stoichiometry problems.

3. Solve stoichiometry problems involving mass by using molar mass.

4. Solve stoichiometry problems involving the volume of a substance by using density.

5. Solve stoichiometry problems involving the number of particles of a substance by using Avogadro's number.

National Science Education Standards Covered

UNIFYING CONCEPTS AND PROCESSES

UCP 1 Systems, order, and organization

UCP 3 Change, constancy, and measurement

UCP 5 Form and function

KEY
SE = Student Edition
ATE = Annotated Teacher Edition

Block 1 *(45 minutes)*

FOCUS *5 minutes*

❑ **Bellringer,** ATE (GENERAL). This activity has students write the ingredients needed to make a sandwich and then determine the quantities of the other ingredients needed if they use 24 slices of bread.

MOTIVATE *5 minutes*

❑ **Identifying Preconceptions,** ATE (GENERAL). Using the equation for water, show students that coefficients in a balanced equation do not indicate masses.

Lesson Plan *continued*

TEACH *35 minutes*

❏ **Skills Toolkit: Converting Between Amounts in Moles,** SE (GENERAL). Use this feature to reinforce the steps of converting between amounts in moles.

❏ **Transparency,** Converting Between Amounts in Moles (GENERAL). This transparency master shows how to convert between amounts in moles using mole ratios. (Skills Toolkit 1)

❏ **Sample Problem A: Using Mole Ratios,** SE (GENERAL). This problem demonstrates how to use mole ratios in calculations.

❏ **Skills Toolkit: Solving Stoichiometry Problems,** SE (GENERAL). Use this feature to walk students through the steps of solving stoichiometry problems.

HOMEWORK

❏ **Reading Skill Builder,** ATE (BASIC). Have students list what they know about how the mass of the reactants affects the mass of the products.

❏ **Practice Sample Problems A: Using Mole Ratios,** SE (GENERAL). Assign items 1–2.

❏ **Homework,** ATE (GENERAL). This assignment provides additional practice problems using mole ratios like those in Practice Problem A.

❏ **Interactive Tutor for ChemFile,** Module 5: Equations and Stoichiometry; Topic: Balancing Equations (GENERAL)

❏ **Interactive Tutor for ChemFile,** Module 5: Equations and Stoichiometry; Topic: Stoichiometry (GENERAL)

OTHER RESOURCES

❏ **Skill Builder,** ATE (BASIC). Have students find balanced chemical equations in the textbook and translate the coefficients to mole ratios.

❏ **Skills Worksheet: Problem Solving–Stoichiometry: Sample Problem 1** (ADVANCED). This worksheet reinforces the problem solving skills developed in Sample Problem A.

❏ **go.hrw.com**

❏ **www.scilinks.org**

Block 2 *(45 minutes)*

TEACH *45 minutes*

❑ **Teaching Tip,** ATE (GENERAL). Emphasize the importance of setting problems up correctly by having students set up problems and cancel units, but not solve the problems. Check that students are indeed setting up problems correctly.

❑ **Skills Toolkit: Solving Mass-Mass Problems,** SE (GENERAL). Use this feature to walk students through the steps of solving mass-mass problems.

❑ **Transparency,** Solving Mass-Mass Problems (GENERAL). This transparency master shows how to solve mass-mass problems. (Skills Toolkit 3)

❑ **Sample Problem B: Problems Involving Mass,** SE (GENERAL). This problem demonstrates how to solve problems involving mass.

HOMEWORK

❑ **Practice Sample Problems B: Problems Involving Mass,** SE (GENERAL). Assign items 1–4.

❑ **Homework,** ATE (GENERAL). This assignment provides additional practice problems involving mass like those in Practice Problem B.

❑ **Interactive Tutor for ChemFile,** Module 5: Equations and Stoichiometry; Topic: Stoichiometry (GENERAL)

OTHER RESOURCES

❑ **Demonstration,** ATE (GENERAL). This demonstration shows students the stoichiometry of a chemical reaction.

❑ **Skills Worksheet: Problem Solving–Stoichiometry: Sample Problems 2, 3, and 4.** (ADVANCED) These worksheets reinforce the problem solving skills developed in Sample Problem B.

❑ **go.hrw.com**

❑ **www.scilinks.org**

Block 3 *(45 minutes)*

TEACH *35 minutes*

❑ **Skills Toolkit: Solving Volume-Volume Problems,** SE (GENERAL). Use this feature to walk students through the steps of solving volume-volume problems.

❑ **Transparency,** Solving Volume-Volume Problems (GENERAL). This transparency master shows how to solve volume-volume problems. (Skills Toolkit 4)

❑ **Sample Problem C: Problems Involving Volume,** SE (GENERAL). This problem demonstrates how to solve problems involving volume.

❑ **Skills Toolkit: Solving Particle Problems,** SE (GENERAL). Use this feature to walk students through the steps of solving particle problems.

❑ **Transparency,** Solving Particle Problems (GENERAL). This transparency master shows how to solve particle problems. (Skills Toolkit 5)

❑ **Sample Problem D: Problems Involving Particles,** SE (GENERAL). This problem demonstrates how to solve problems involving particles.

CLOSE *10 minutes*

❑ **Reteaching,** ATE (BASIC). Students make a model that demonstrates all of the steps for solving stoichiometry problems discussed in Section 1.

❑ **Quiz,** ATE (GENERAL). This assignment has students answer questions about the concepts in this lesson. Questions 1 and 2 are problems.

❑ **Assessment Worksheet: Section Quiz** (GENERAL)

HOMEWORK

❑ **Practice Sample Problems C: Problems Involving Volume,** SE (GENERAL). Assign items 1–4.

❑ **Practice Sample Problems D: Problems Involving Particles,** SE (GENERAL). Assign items 1–2.

❑ **Homework,** ATE (GENERAL). This assignment provides additional practice problems involving particles like those in Practice Problem D.

❑ **Section Review,** SE (GENERAL). Assign items 1–7.

❑ **Skills Worksheet: Concept Review** (GENERAL)

❑ **Interactive Tutor for ChemFile,** Module: Equations and Stoichiometry; Topic: Stoichiometry

OTHER RESOURCES

❑ **Homework,** ATE (ADVANCED). This assignment provides additional practice problems involving volume like those in Practice Problem C.

❑ **go.hrw.com**

❑ **www.scilinks.org**

Lesson Plan

Section: Limiting Reactants and Percent Yield

Pacing

Regular Schedule	**with lab(s):** 6 days	**without lab(s):** 2 days
Block Schedule	**with lab(s):** 3 days	**without lab(s):** 1 day

Objectives

1. Identify the limiting reactant for a reaction and use it to calculate theoretical yield.

2. Perform calculations involving percentage yield.

National Science Education Standards Covered

UNIFYING CONCEPTS AND PROCESSES

UCP 1 Systems, order, and organization

UCP 3 Change, constancy, and measurement

UCP 5 Form and function

> **KEY**
> **SE** = Student Edition
> **ATE** = Annotated Teacher Edition

Block 4 *(45 minutes)*

FOCUS *5 minutes*

❏ **Bellringer,** ATE (GENERAL). This activity has students discuss with a partner the difference between ideal yield and actual yield.

MOTIVATE *10 minutes*

❏ **Demonstration,** ATE (GENERAL). This demonstration has students model limiting and excess materials.

TEACH *30 minutes*

❏ **Demonstration,** ATE (GENERAL). This demonstration illustrates the concept of limiting reactants.

❏ **Sample Problem E: Limiting Reactants and Theoretical Yield,** SE (GENERAL). This problem demonstrates how to identify the limiting reactant and theoretical yield of a given chemical reaction.

HOMEWORK

❏ **Practice Sample Problem E: Limiting Reactants and Theoretical Yield,** SE (GENERAL). Assign items 1–3.

❏ **Homework,** ATE (GENERAL). This assignment gives students additional practice identifying the limiting reactant and theoretical yield of a given chemical reaction. (Sample Problem E)

OTHER RESOURCES

❏ **Demonstration,** ATE (GENERAL). This demonstration uses marble chips and acid to illustrate a number of concepts including theoretical and actual yield.

❏ **Skills Worksheet: Problem Solving–Limiting Reactants: Sample Problems 1 and 2.** (ADVANCED) These worksheets reinforce the problem solving skills developed in Sample Problem E.

❏ **Interactive Tutor for ChemFile,** Module: Equations and Stoichiometry; Topic: Limiting Reagents (GENERAL)

❏ **go.hrw.com**

❏ **www.scilinks.org**

Block 5 *(45 minutes)*

TEACH *35 minutes*

❏ **Sample Problem F: Calculating Percentage Yield,** SE (GENERAL). This problem demonstrates how to calculate percentage yield.

❏ **Sample Problem G: Calculating Actual Yield,** SE (GENERAL). This problem demonstrates how to calculate actual yield.

❏ **Datasheets for In-text Lab: Stoichiometry and Gravimetric Analysis,** SE (GENERAL). Students relate the mass of precipitate formed to the mass of the reactants before the reaction.

❏ **Datasheets for In-text Lab: Gravimetric Analysis—Hard-Water Testing,** SE (GENERAL). Students perform stoichiometric calculations to determine the mass of calcium ions present in a solution and determine whether a water sample should be classified as hard water.

CLOSE *10 minutes*

❏ **Quiz,** ATE (GENERAL). This assignment has students answer questions about the concepts in this lesson.

❏ **Reteaching,** ATE (BASIC). Students use a model kit to model reactions that have a limiting reactant.

❏ **Assessment Worksheet: Section Quiz** (GENERAL)

HOMEWORK

❑ **Practice Sample Problems F: Calculating Percentage Yield,** SE (GENERAL). Assign items 1–3.

❑ **Homework,** ATE (GENERAL). This assignment gives students additional practice calculating percentage yield. (Sample Problem F).

❑ **Practice Sample Problems G: Calculating Actual Yield,** SE (GENERAL). Assign items 1–3.

❑ **Homework,** ATE (GENERAL). This assignment gives students additional practice calculating actual yield. (Sample Problem G).

❑ **Skills Worksheet: Concept Review** (GENERAL)

❑ **Section Review,** SE (GENERAL). Assign items 1–14.

❑ **Interactive Tutor for ChemFile,** Module 5: Equations and Stoichiometry; Topic: Stoichiometry (GENERAL)

OTHER RESOURCES

❑ **Group Activity,** ATE (GENERAL). This activity has students brainstorm analogies for calculating percentage yield and generate their own problems.

❑ **Skills Worksheet: Problem Solving–Percent Yield: Sample Problems 1 and 2.** (ADVANCED) These worksheets reinforce the problem solving skills developed in Sample Problem F.

❑ **go.hrw.com**

❑ **www.scilinks.org**

Lesson Plan

Section: Stoichiometry and Cars

Pacing

Regular Schedule	**with lab(s):** NA	**without lab(s):** 2 days
Block Schedule	**with lab(s):** NA	**without lab(s):** 1 day

Objectives

1. Relate volume calculations in stoichiometry to the inflation of automobile safety air bags.

2. Use the concept of limiting reactants to explain why fuel-air ratios affect engine performance.

3. Compare the efficiency of pollution-control mechanisms in cars using percentage yield.

National Science Education Standards Covered

UNIFYING CONCEPTS AND PROCESSES

UCP 1 Systems, order, and organization

UCP 3 Change, constancy, and measurement

UCP 5 Form and function

PHYSICAL SCIENCE—CHEMICAL REACTIONS

PS 3a Chemical reactions occur all around us, for example in health care, cooking, cosmetics, and automobiles. Complex chemical reactions involving carbon-based molecules take place constantly in every cell in our bodies.

> **KEY**
> **SE** = Student Edition
> **ATE** = Annotated Teacher Edition

Block 6 *(45 minutes)*

FOCUS *5 minutes*

❑ **Bellringer,** ATE (GENERAL). Students brainstorm chemical reactions that are involved in operating a car.

MOTIVATE *5 minutes*

❑ **Discussion,** ATE (GENERAL). Invite students to share their experiences with automobile air bags as a guide for the air bag segment of this section.

TEACH *35 minutes*

❑ **Skill Builder,** ATE (GENERAL). Use Figure 6 to discuss the mechanism, pros, and cons of air bags in cars.

❑ **Sample Problem H: Air Bag Stoichiometry,** SE (GENERAL). This problem demonstrates how to solve stoichiometric problems that relate to air bags.

❑ **Transparency,** Fuel-Oxygen Ratio (GENERAL). This transparency master illustrates how the fuel-oxygen ratio changes depending on what the engine is doing. (Figure 7)

❑ **Skill Builder,** ATE (GENERAL). Use Figure 7 to discuss how gas burns in a car engine.

HOMEWORK

❑ **Practice Sample Problems H: Air Bag Stoichiometry,** SE (GENERAL). Assign items 1–4.

❑ **Homework,** ATE (ADVANCED). This assignment has students solve problems related to air bags. (Practice Problem H)

OTHER RESOURCES

❑ **Skill Builder,** ATE (ADVANCED). Have students research statistics related to the use of air bags in cars.

❑ **go.hrw.com**

❑ **www.scilinks.org**

Block 7 *(45 minutes)*
TEACH *30 minutes*

❑ **Sample Problem I: Air-Fuel Ratio,** SE (GENERAL). This problem demonstrates how to solve stoichiometric problems that relate to air-fuel ratio.

❑ **Reading Skill Builder,** ATE (BASIC). Based on their reading of the text, students draw a graphic organizer that shows how catalytic converters work.

❑ **Sample Problem J: Calculating Yields: Pollution,** SE (GENERAL). This problem demonstrates how to calculate yields related to car pollution.

CLOSE *15 minutes*

❑ **Reteaching,** ATE (BASIC). Students write a paragraph that describes how stoichiometry relates to cars.

❑ **Quiz,** ATE (GENERAL). This assignment has students answer questions about the concepts in this lesson.

❑ **Assessment Worksheet: Section Quiz** (GENERAL)

HOMEWORK

❑ **Skills Worksheet: Concept Review** (GENERAL) This worksheet reviews the main concepts and problem-solving skills of this section by having students do this worksheet in class.

❑ **Practice Sample Problems I: Air-Fuel Ratio,** SE (GENERAL). Assign students items 1–3.

❑ **Homework,** ATE (GENERAL). This assignment has students solve problems related to air-fuel ratio. (Practice Problem I)

❑ **Practice Sample Problems J: Calculating Yields: Pollution,** SE (GENERAL). Assign item 1.

❑ **Homework,** ATE (GENERAL). This assignment has students solve problems related to the pollution created by racecars. (Practice Problem J)

❑ **Section Review,** SE (GENERAL). Assign items 1–9.

❑ **Interactive Tutor for ChemFile,** Module 5: Equations and Stoichiometry, Topic: Stoichiometry (GENERAL)

OTHER RESOURCES

❑ **Skill Builder,** ATE (ADVANCED). Have students write a paragraph that relates automobile ratings in miles per gallon to percentage yield of the combustion reaction.

❑ **go.hrw.com**

❑ **www.scilinks.org**

END OF CHAPTER REVIEW AND ASSESSMENT RESOURCES

❑ **Mixed Review,** SE (GENERAL).

❑ **Alternate Assessment,** SE (GENERAL).

❑ **Focus on Graphing,** SE (GENERAL).

❑ **Technology and Learning,** SE (GENERAL).

❑ **Standardized Test Prep,** SE (GENERAL).

❑ **Assessment Worksheet: Chapter Test** (GENERAL)

❑ **Test Item Listing for ExamView® Test Generator**

Name _____ Class _____ Date _____

Stoichiometry and Gravimetric Analysis

You are working for a company that makes water-softening agents for homes with hard water. Recently, there was a mix-up on the factory floor, and sodium carbonate solution was mistakenly mixed in a vat with an unknown quantity of distilled water. You must determine the amount of Na_2CO_3 in the vat in order to properly predict the percentage yield of the water-softening product.

When chemists are faced with problems that require them to determine the quantity of a substance by mass, they often use a technique called gravimetric analysis. In this technique, a small sample of the material undergoes a reaction with an excess of another reactant. The chosen reaction is one that almost always provides a yield near 100%. In other words, all of the reactant of unknown amount will be converted into product. If the mass of the product is carefully measured, you can use stoichiometry calculations to determine how much of the reactant of unknown amount was involved in the reaction. Then by comparing the size of the analysis sample with the size of the original material, you can determine exactly how much of the substance is present.

This procedure involves a double-displacement reaction between strontium chloride, $SrCl_2$, and sodium carbonate, Na_2CO_3. In general, this reaction can be used to determine the amount of any carbonate compound in a solution.

Remember that accurate results depend on precise mass measurements. Keep all glassware very clean, and do not lose any reactants or products during your lab work.

You will react an unknown amount of sodium carbonate with an excess of strontium chloride. After purifying the product, you will determine the following:

- how much product is present
- how much Na_2CO_3 must have been present to produce that amount of product
- how much Na_2CO_3 is contained in the 575 L of solution

OBJECTIVES

Observe the reaction between strontium chloride and sodium carbonate, and write a balanced equation for the reaction.

Demonstrate proficiency with gravimetric methods.

Measure the mass of insoluble precipitate formed.

Draw conclusions and relate the mass of precipitate formed to the mass of reactants before the reaction.

Calculate the mass of sodium carbonate in a solution of unknown concentration.

Name _____ Class _____ Date _____

Stoichiometry and Gravimetric Analysis *continued*

MATERIALS

- balance
- beaker tongs
- beakers, 250 mL (3)
- distilled water
- drying oven
- filter paper
- glass funnel or Büchner funnel
- glass stirring rod

- graduated cylinder, 100 mL
- Na_2CO_3 solution
- ring and ring stand
- rubber policeman
- spatula
- $SrCl_2$ solution, 0.30 M
- water bottle

Always wear safety goggles and a lab apron to protect your eyes and clothing. If you get a chemical in your eyes, immediately flush the chemical out at the eyewash station while calling to your teacher. Know the location of the emergency lab shower and eyewash station and the procedures for using them.

Do not touch any chemicals. If you get a chemical on your skin or clothing, wash the chemical off at the sink while calling to your teacher. Make sure you carefully read the labels and follow the precautions on all containers of chemicals that you use. If there are no precautions stated on the label, ask your teacher what precautions to follow. Do not taste any chemicals or items used in the laboratory. Never return leftovers to their original container; take only small amounts to avoid wasting supplies.

Do not heat glassware that is broken, chipped, or cracked. Use tongs or a hot mitt to handle heated glassware and other equipment because hot glassware does not always look hot.

Procedure

1. Put on safety goggles and lab apron.

2. Clean all of the necessary lab equipment with soap and water. Rinse each piece of equipment with distilled water.

3. Measure the mass of a piece of filter paper to the nearest 0.01 g, and record this value in your data table.

4. Set up a filtering apparatus, either a Büchner funnel or a gravity filtration, depending on what equipment is available.

5. Label a paper towel with your name, your class, and the date. Place the towel in a clean, dry 250 mL beaker, and measure and record the mass of the towel and beaker to the nearest 0.01 g.

6. Measure about 15 mL of the Na_2CO_3 solution into the graduated cylinder. Record this volume to the nearest 0.5 mL in your data table. Pour the Na_2CO_3 solution into a clean, empty 250 mL beaker. Carefully wash the graduated cylinder, and rinse it with distilled water.

7. Measure about 25 mL of the 0.30 M $SrCl_2$ solution into the graduated cylinder. Record this volume to the nearest 0.5 mL in your data table. Pour the $SrCl_2$ solution into the beaker with the Na_2CO_3 solution. Gently stir the solution and precipitate with a glass stirring rod.

8. Carefully measure another 10 mL of $SrCl_2$ into the graduated cylinder. Record the volume to the nearest 0.5 mL in your data table. Slowly add it to the beaker. Repeat this step until no more precipitate forms.

9. Once the precipitate has settled, slowly pour the mixture into the funnel. Be careful not to overfill the funnel because some of the precipitate could be lost between the filter paper and the funnel. Use the rubber policeman to transfer as much of the precipitate into the funnel as possible.

10. Rinse the rubber policeman into the beaker with a small amount of distilled water, and pour this solution into the funnel. Rinse the beaker several more times with small amounts of distilled water. Pour the rinse water into the funnel each time.

11. After all of the solution and rinses have drained through the funnel, slowly rinse the precipitate on the filter paper in the funnel with distilled water to remove any soluble impurities.

12. Carefully remove the filter paper from the funnel, and place it on the paper towel that you have labeled with your name. Unfold the filter paper, and place the paper towel, filter paper, and precipitate in the rinsed beaker. Then place the beaker in the drying oven. For best results, allow the precipitate to dry overnight.

13. Using beaker tongs, remove your sample from the drying oven, and allow it to cool. Measure and record the mass of the beaker with paper towel, filter paper, and precipitate to the nearest 0.01 g.

14. Dispose of the precipitate in a designated waste container. Pour the filtrate in the other 250 mL beaker into the designated waste container. Clean up the lab and all equipment after use, and dispose of substances according to your teacher's instructions. Wash your hands thoroughly after all lab work is finished and before you leave the lab.

TABLE 1 GRAVIMETRIC ANALYSIS DATA

Volume of Na_2CO_3 solution added	**15 mL**
Volume of $SrCl_2$ solution added	**35 mL**
Mass of dry filter paper	**0.30 g**
Mass of beaker with paper towel	**186.55 g**
Mass of beaker with paper towel, filter paper, and precipitate	**187.91 g**
Mass of precipitate	**1.06 g**

Analysis

1. **Organizing Data** Write a balanced equation for the reaction. What is the precipitate? Write its empirical formula. (Hint: It was a double-displacement reaction.)

   $SrCl_2(aq) + Na_2CO_3(aq) \rightarrow 2\ NaCl(aq) + SrCO_3(s)$

   The precipitate is strontium carbonate, $SrCO_3$

2. **Examining Data** Calculate the mass of the dry precipitate. Calculate the number of moles of precipitate produced in the reaction. (Hint: Use the results from step 13.)

   Answers will vary for mass of the dry precipitate. According to the sample data given in the ATE, the calculated mass for $SrCO_3$ is 1.06 g.

   1.06 g $SrCO_3$ × 1 mol $SrCO_3$/147.63 g $SrCO_3$ = 7.18 × 10^{-3} mol $SrCO_3$

3. **Examining Data** How many moles of Na_2CO_3 were present in the 15 mL sample?

   **7.18 × 10^{-3} mol $SrCO_3$ × 1 mol Na_2CO_3/1 mol $SrCO_3$ =
   7.18 × 10^{-3} mol Na_2CO_3**

Stoichiometry and Gravimetric Analysis *continued*

Conclusions

4. **Evaluating Methods** There was 0.30 mol of $SrCl_2$ in every liter of solution. Calculate the number of moles of $SrCl_2$ that were added. Determine whether $SrCl_2$ or Na_2CO_3 was the limiting reactant. Would this experiment have worked if the other reactant had been chosen as the limiting reactant? Explain why or why not.

35 mL $SrCl_2$ × 1 L/1000 mL × 0.30 mol/1 L = 1.05 × 10^{-2} mol $SrCl_2$

Sodium carbonate is the limiting reactant. Only sodium carbonate could be

used as the limiting reactant, because the purpose of the experiment was to

use gravimetric analysis to determine the amount of sodium carbonate in

solution. If another reactant had been used as the limiting reactant, the

mass of Na_2CO_3 in solution could not have been determined before the

reaction went to completion.

5. **Evaluating Methods** Why was the precipitate rinsed in step 11? What soluble impurities could have been on the filter paper along with the precipitate? How would the calculated results vary if the precipitate had not been completely dry? Explain your answer.

The precipitate was rinsed to remove any NaCl impurities that may have

remained on the $SrCO_3$.

_____

6. **Applying Conclusions** How many grams of Na_2CO_3 were present in the 15 mL sample?
7.18 × 10^{-3} mol Na_2CO_3 × 105.99 g Na_2CO_3/1 mol Na_2CO_3 =
0.761 g Na_2CO_3/15 mL

7. **Applying Conclusions** How many grams of Na_2CO_3 are present in the 575 L? (Hint: Create a conversion factor to convert from the sample, with a volume of 15 mL, to the entire solution, with a volume of 575 L.)
575 L × 0.761 g Na_2CO_3/15 mL × 1000 mL/1L = 2.74 × 104 g Na_2CO_3

Stoichiometry and Gravimetric Analysis *continued*

8. Evaluating Methods Ask your teacher for the theoretical mass of Na_2CO_3 in the sample, and calculate your percentage error.

Using a 0.5 M solution, the correct mass of Na_2CO_3 is 0.795 g for every 15.0 mL.

Extensions

1. Designing Experiments What possible sources of error can you identify with your procedure? If you can think of ways to eliminate them, ask your teacher to approve your plan, and run the procedure again.

Suggestions for improving the procedure will vary. Students may suggest

using larger amounts of each reactant or running multiple trials. Be sure

experiments are safe and include carefully planned procedures.

Gravimetric Analysis—Hard-Water Testing

Teacher Notes

MATERIALS

- balance
- beaker tongs
- beakers, 250 mL (2)
- $CaCl_2$ solution (20 mL)
- drying oven

- graduated cylinder, 100 mL
- Na_2CO_3, 0.5 M (75 mL or less)
- pipe-stem triangle
- ring and ring stand

ANSWERS

Procedure

Measure the mass of a piece of filter paper and a beaker. Add an excess of Na_2CO_3 solution of known concentration to a carefully measured volume of the solution containing calcium ions. Filter and dry the $CaCO_3$ precipitate that forms. Measure its mass.

SAMPLE DATA

Volume of water sample	20.00 mL
Volume of 0.5 M Na_2CO_3	40.00 mL
Mass of 150 mL beaker	65.80 mL
Mass of filter paper	0.31 g
Mass of beaker, filter paper, and $CaCO_3$	67.07 g
Mass of $CaCO_3$	0.96

Calculations

Mass of calcium = 0.96 g $CaCO_3$ × 40 g Ca/100g = 0.38 g Ca

Concentration of Ca = 0.38 g/1L (original volume) = 380 mg/L

Water is hard

Answer Key

Concept Review: Calculating Quantities in Reactions

1. mole
2. balance
3. relative
4. coefficients
5. molar mass
6. liquids
7. density
8. Avogadro's number
9. c
10. b
11. b
12. c
13. c
14. 1.00 g $Ca_3(PO_4)_2$ ×
    1 mol $Ca_3(PO_4)_2$/310.18 g $Ca_3(PO_4)_2$
    × 2 mol P/1 mol $Ca_3(PO_4)_2$
    × 30.97 g P/1 mol P = 0.200 g P
15. 18 g Al × 1 mol Al/26.98 g Al
    × 2 mol $AlCl_3$/2 mol Al
    × 133.33 g $AlCl_3$/1 mol $AlCl_3$ =
    89 g $AlCl_3$
16. 1150 g $C_6H_{12}O_6$ × 1 mol
    $C_6H_{12}O_6$/180.18 g $C_6H_{12}O_6$
    × 2 mol C_2H_5OH/1 mol $C_6H_{12}O_6$
    × 46.08 g C_2H_5OH/1 mol C_2H_5OH
    = 588 g C_2H_5OH
17. 25.5 g Mg × 1 mol Mg/24.30 g Mg
    × 1 mol O_2/2 mol Mg
    = 0.525 mol O_2
18. 1.0 mol $C_5H_{11}OH$ × 10 mol CO_2/2 mol
    $C_5H_{11}OH$ × 44.01 g CO_2/1 mol CO_2
    = 220 g CO_2
19. 500.0 g CCl_3NO_2 × 1 mol
    CCl_3NO_2/164.37 g CCl_3NO_2 × 1 mol
    CH_3NO_2/1 mol CCl_3NO_2 =
    3.042 mol CH_3NO_2
20. 122 g $KClO_3$ × 1 mol $KClO_3$/122.55 g
    $KClO_3$ × 32.00 g O_2/1 mol O_2 × 3 mol
    O_2/2 mol $KClO_3$ × 1 L O_2/1.33 g O_2 =
    35.9 L O_2
21. 3.4 L O_2 × 1.33 g O_2/1 L O_2 × 1 mol
    O_2/32.00 g O_2 × 2 mol KCl/3 mol O_2 ×
    74.55 g KCl/1 mol KCl = 7.0 g KCl

22. 910 g Ca_3P_2 × 1 mol Ca_3P_2/182.18 g
    Ca_3P_2 × 2 mol PH_3/1 mol Ca_3P_2 ×
    33.99 g PH_3/1 mol PH_3 × 1 L
    PH_3/1.517 g PH_3 = 220 L PH_3
23. 93 g P × 1 mol P/30.97 g P × 5 mol
    O_2/4 mol P × 32.00 g O_2/1 mol O_2 ×
    100. g air/23 g O_2 = 520 g air
24. 5.00 metric tons coke × 85.5%
    C/100.0% coke × 1.00 × 10^6 g/1 metric
    ton × 44.01 g CO_2/1 mol CO_2 × 1 mol
    C/12.01 g C × 1 mol CO_2/1 mol C ×
    1 metric ton/1.00 × 10^6 g = 15.7 metric
    tons CO_2
25. 100 mL CS_2 × 1.26 g CS_2/1 mL CS_2 ×
    1 mol CS_2/76.15 g CS_2 × 2 mol SO_2/1
    mol CS_2 × 22.4 L SO_2/1 mol SO_2 =
    74.1 L SO_2 74.01 L SO_2 × 1 mol CO_2/2
    mol SO_2 = 37.1 L CO_2

Concept Review: Limiting Reactants and Percentage Yield

1. excess
2. limiting, product
3. limiting
4. stoichiometric
5. limiting
6. excess
7. percentage
8. actual; theoretical
9. actual
10. actual
11. 3.00 g Mg × (1 mol Mg/24.30 g Mg) =
    0.123 mol Mg
    2.20 g O_2 × (1 mol O_2/32.00 g O_2) =
    0.688 mol O_2
    0.0688 mol O_2 × (2 mol Mg/1 mol O_2)
    = 0.138 mol Mg needed.
    Mg is limiting.
    0.123 mol Mg × (2 mol MgO/2 mol Mg)
    × (40.30 g MgO/1 mol MgO) = 4.96 g
    MgO

86

12. 23 g $C_2H_5OH \times$ (1 mol C_2H_5OH/46.08 g C_2H_5OH) = 0.50 mol C_2H_5OH

32 g $O_2 \times$ (1 mol O_2/32.00 g O_2) = 1.0 mol O_2

1.0 mol $O_2 \times$ (1 mol C_2H_5OH/3 mol O_2) = 0.33 mol C_2H_5OH needed

O_2 is limiting.

1.0 mol $O_2 \times$ (2 mol CO_2/3 mol O_2) $\times$ (44.01 g CO_2/1 mol CO_2) = 29 g CO_2

13. 154 g Ag $\times$ (1 mol Ag/107.87 g Ag) = 1.43 mol Ag

189 g $HNO_3 \times$ (1 mol HNO_3/63.02 g HNO_3) = 3.00 mol HNO_3

3.00 mol $HNO_3 \times$ (3 mol Ag/4 mol HNO_3) = 2.25 mol Ag needed

Ag is limiting.

1.43 mol Ag $\times$ (3 mol $AgNO_3$/3 mol Ag) $\times$ (169.88 g $AgNO_3$/1 mol $AgNO_3$) = 243 g $AgNO_3$

14. 1.34 g Ag $\times$ (1 mol Ag/107.87 g Ag) $\times$ (3 mol $AgNO_3$/3 mol Ag) $\times$ (169.88 g $AgNO_3$/1 mol $AgNO_3$) = 2.11 g $AgNO_3$

percentage yield = (actual yield/theoretical yield) x 100

(2.10 g $AgNO_3$ actual yield/2.11 g $AgNO_3$ theoretical yield) $\times$ 100 = 95.3%

15. 5.552 g $Pb(NO_3)_2 \times$ (1 mol $Pb(NO_3)_2$/331.2 g $Pb(NO_3)_2$) $\times$ (1 mol $PbCrO_4$/1 mol $Pb(NO_3)_2$) $\times$ (323.2 g $PbCrO_4$/1 mol $PbCrO_4$)

percentage yield = (actual yield/theoretical yield) $\times$ 100 = (5.096 g $PbCrO_4$/5.418 g $PbCrO_4$) $\times$ 100 = 94.06%

16. 20.0 g Mg $\times$ (1 mol Mg/24.30 g Mg) $\times$ (2 mol MgO/2 mol Mg) $\times$ (40.30 g MgO/1 mol MgO) $\times$ (97.9% percentage yield/100% theoretical yield) = 32.5 g MgO

17. 10.0 g FeS $\times$ (1 mol FeS/87.92 g FeS) $\times$ (2 mol Fe_2O_3/4 mol FeS) $\times$ (159.70 g Fe_2O_3/1 mol Fe_2O_3) = 9.08 g Fe_2O_3 theoretical yield

9.08 g $Fe_2O_3 \times$ (88.1 % percentage yield/100% theoretical yield) = 8.00 g Fe_2O_3

18. 175.0 g $Cl_2 \times$ (1 mol Cl_2/70.90 g Cl_2) $\times$ (1 mol CCl_4/4 mol Cl_2) $\times$ (153.81 g CCl_4/1 mol CCl_4) $\times$ (75.4% actual yield/100% theoretical yield) = 71.6 g CCl_4

Concept Review: Stoichiometry and Cars

1. c
2. b
3. d
4. b
5. d
6. If there is too much oxygen and not enough gasoline, the engine will stall. If, on the other hand, gasoline is in excess and there is not enough oxygen, lack of oxygen may prevent the mixture from igniting.
7. 68.0 L $N_2 \times$ (0.916 g N_2/1 L N_2) $\times$ (1 mol N_2/28.02 g N_2) $\times$ (2 mol NaN_3/3 mol N_2) $\times$ (65.02 g NaN_3/1 mol NaN_3) = 96.4 g NaN_3
8. 375 mL $C_8H_{18} \times$ (0.692 g C_8H_{18}/1 mL C_8H_{18}) $\times$ (1 mol C_8H_{18}/114.26 g C_8H_{18}) $\times$ (25 mol O_2/2 mol C_8H_{18}) $\times$ (32.00 g O_2/1 mol O_2) $\times$ (1 L O_2/1.33 g O_2) $\times$ (100 g air/23 g O_2) = 2.97 $\times$ 10^3 g air
9. 4.30 g $NO_2 \times$ (1 mol NO_2/46.01 g NO_2) $\times$ (1 mol O_3/1 mol NO_2) $\times$ (48.00 g O_3/1 mol O_3) = 4.49 g O_3
10. octane: (2.5 L)(0.700 g/ml)(1000 ml/1 L) = (2.5)(700 g) = 1750 g

MW octane = 114.231 g/ml

2.5 L octane = (1750 g)(1 mol/114.23092) = 15.319845 mol

2.5 L octane yields 8(15.319845 mol) = 122.559 mol CO_2

MW CO_2 = 44.0098 g/mol

(122.559 mol CO_2)(44.0098 g/mol) = 5394 g CO_2

Additional Problems

STOICHIOMETRY

1. 15.0 mol $(NH_4)_2SO_4$
2. a. 51 g Al
b. 101 g Fe
c. 1.83 mol Fe_2O_3
3. 0.303 g H_2
4. $H_2SO_4 + 2KOH \rightarrow K_2SO_4 + 2H_2O$; 1.11 g H_2SO_4
5. a. $H_3PO_4 + 2NH_3 \rightarrow (NH_4)_2HPO_4$
b. 0.293 mol $(NH_4)_2HPO_4$
c. 970 kg NH_3
6. a. 90.0 mol $ZnCO_3$; 60.0 mol $C_6H_8O_7$
b. 13.5 kg H_2O; 33.0 kg CO_2

7. a. 60.9 g methyl butanoate
  b. 3261 g H_2O
8. a. 0.450 mol N_2
  b. 294 g NH_4NO_3
9. $Pb(NO_3)_2 + 2KI \rightarrow PbI_2 + 2KNO_3$; 0.751 mg KNO_3
10. 3.3 mol $PbSO_4$
11. $2LiOH + CO_2 \rightarrow H_2O + Li_2CO_3$; 360 g H_2O
12. a. 38.1 g H_2O
  b. 40.1 g H_3PO_4
  c. 0.392 mol H_2O
13. $C_2H_5OH + 3O_2 \rightarrow 2CO_2 + 3H_2O$; 81.0 g C_2H_5OH
14. 76.5 g H_2SO_4; 12.5 g O_2
15. $2NaHCO_3 \rightarrow Na_2CO_3 + H_2O + CO_2$; 1.31 g CO_2
16. a. $2N_2H_4 + N_2O_4 \rightarrow 3N_2 + 4H_2O$
  b. 1 mol N_2O_4 to 3 mol N_2
  c. 30 000 mol N_2
  d. 3.52×10^5 g H_2O
17. $2HgO(s) \rightarrow 2Hg(l) + O_2(g)$; 1.1954 mol O_2
18. $2Fe + 3Cl_2 \rightarrow 2FeCl_3$; 30.5 g Fe
19. 9.26 mg CdS
20. a. 1.59 mol CO_2
  b. 0.0723 mol $C_3H_5(OH)_3$
  c. 535 g Mn_2O_3
  d. 8.33 g $C_3H_5(OH)_3$; 4.97 g CO_2
21. a. 3.29×10^3 kg of HCl
  b. 330 g CO_2 (s)
22. a. 6.53×10^5 g NH_4ClO_4
  b. 160 kg NO(g)
23. a. 1.70×10^6 mol H_3PO_4
  b. 666 kg of $CaSO_4 \cdot 2H_2O$
  c. 34 metric tons of H_3PO_4
24. 1670 kg

LIMITING REACTANTS
1. $2ZnS + 3O_2 \rightarrow 2ZnO + 2SO_2$; ZnS is limiting
2. a. Al is limiting
  b. 4.25×10^{-3} mol Al_2O_3
  c. O_2 is limiting
3. a. CuS is limiting
  b. 15.6 g CuO
4. Fe is limiting; 0.158 mol Cu
5. 54 g $Ba(NO_3)_2$
6. a. 38 g Br_2
  b. 510 g I_2
7. a. Ni is in excess
  b. 60.2 g $Ni(NO_3)_2$

8. $CS_2(g) + 3O_2(g) \rightarrow 2SO_4(g) + CO_2(g)$
  0.80 mol O_2 remain
9. a. 0.84 g $Hg(NH_2)Cl$
  b. 0.84 g
10. a. $2Al(s) + 2NaOH(aq) + 2H_2O(l) \rightarrow 2NaAlO_2(aq) + 3H_2(g)$
  b. NaOH is limiting; 0.56 mol H_2
  c. Al should be limiting because you would not want aluminum metal remaining in the drain.
11. a. 0.0422 mol Cu; 0.169 mol HNO_3
  b. Cu is in excess
  c. 3.32 g H_2O
12. a. 2.90 mol NO;
    4.35 mol H_2O
  b. NH_3 is limiting
  c. NH_3 is limiting; 1.53×10^3 kg NO
13. 565 g CH_3CHO;
  29 g CH_3CH_2OH remains
14. 630 g HBr
15. 12.7 g SO_2
16. a. 18.4 g Tb
  b. 2.4 g TbF_3

PERCENTAGE YIELD
1. a. 64.3% yield
  b. 58.0% yield
  c. 69.5% yield
  d. CH_3CH_2OH is limiting; 79% yield
2. a. 69.5% yield
  b. 79.0% yield
  c. 48% yield
  d. 85% yield
3. a. 59% yield
  b. 81.0% yield
  c. 2.3×10^5 mol P
4. a. 91.8% yield
  b. 0.0148 mol W
  c. 16.1 g WO_3
5. a. 86.8% yield
  b. 92.2% yield
  c. 2.97×10^4 kg CS_2;
    4.39×10^4 kg S_2Cl_2
6. a. 81% yield
  b. 2.0×10^2 g N_2O_5
7. 80.1% yield
8. a. 95% yield
  b. 9.10×10^2 g Au
  c. 9×10^4 kg ore
9. a. 87.5% yield
  b. 0.25 g CO
10. a. 71% yield
  b. 26 metric tons

c. 47.8 g NaCl

d. 500 kg per hour NaOH

11. a. $2Mg + O_2 \rightarrow 2MgO$

   b. 87.7% yield

   c. $3Mg + N_2 \rightarrow Mg_3N_2$

   d. 56% yield

12. a. 80.% yield

   b. 66.2% yield

   c. 57.1% yield

13. $2C_3H_6(g) + 2NH_3(g) + 3O_2(g) \rightarrow$
   $2C_3H_3N(g) + 6H_2O(g)$
   91.0% yield

14. a. $CO + 2H_2 \rightarrow CH_3OH$
   3.41×10^3 kg

   b. 91.5% yield

15. 96.9% yield

16. $6CO_2 + 6H_2O \rightarrow C_6H_{12}O_6 + 6O_2$
   6.32×10^3 g O_2

17. 27.6 kg CaO

Answer Key

Quiz—Section: Calculating Quantities in Reactions

1. d	6. c
2. c	7. a
3. c	8. c
4. d	9. c
5. b	10. c

Quiz—Section: Limiting Reactants and Percentage Yield

1. b	6. c
2. d	7. a
3. c	8. d
4. c	9. d
5. b	10. b

Quiz—Section: Stoichiometry and Cars

1. b	6. d
2. c	7. b
3. c	8. a
4. c	9. b
5. c	10. b

Chapter Test

1. d	11. d
2. d	12. b
3. b	13. a
4. d	14. d
5. a	15. a
6. c	16. c
7. b	17. c
8. a	18. b
9. a	19. d
10. a	20. a

21. Thirty percent of the expected product is not produced. Therefore, thirty percent of the limiting reactant must be part of reverse or side reactions.

22. Moles are used because the coefficients in a balanced equation show the number of moles of reactants and products in the chemical reaction.

23. The equation does not show other components of air, such as nitrogen and organic compounds. It also does not show impurities in gasoline, such as compounds of nitrogen and sulfur. During combustion, these substances are also oxidized, producing pollutants such as nitrogen, sulfur oxides, and hydrocarbons. In addition, the equation does not show that incomplete combustion can occur, in which case carbon monoxide is also produced.

24. $100. \text{ g KClO}_3 \times \dfrac{1 \text{ mol KClO}_3}{122.5 \text{ g KClO}_3}$

$\times \dfrac{2 \text{ mol KCl}}{1 \text{ mol KClO}_3} \times \dfrac{74.55 \text{ g KCl}}{1 \text{ mol KCl}}$

$= 60.8 \text{ g KCl}$

25. $65.0 \text{ L CO}_2 \times \dfrac{1.961 \text{ g CO}_2}{1 \text{ L CO}_2}$

$\times \dfrac{1 \text{ mol CO}_2}{44.01 \text{ g CO}_2} \times \dfrac{1 \text{ mol MgCO}_3}{1 \text{ mol CO}_2}$

$\times \dfrac{84.31 \text{ g MgCO}_3}{1 \text{ mol MgCO}_3} = 244 \text{ g MgCO}_3$

Stoichiometry

MULTIPLE CHOICE

1. A balanced chemical equation allows one to determine the
   a. mole ratio of any two substances in the reaction.
   b. energy released in the reaction.
   c. electron configuration of all elements in the reaction.
   d. mechanism involved in the reaction.
   Answer: A   Difficulty: I   Section: 1   Objective: 1

2. The coefficients in a chemical equation represent the
   a. masses, in grams, of all reactants and products.
   b. relative numbers of moles of reactants and products.
   c. number of atoms in each compound in a reaction.
   d. number of valence electrons involved in the reaction.
   Answer: B   Difficulty: I   Section: 1   Objective: 1

3. How many mole ratios can be correctly obtained from the chemical equation
   $2NO \rightarrow N_2 + O_2$?
   a. 1   c. 4
   b. 3   d. 6
   Answer: D   Difficulty: II   Section: 1   Objective: 1

4. In the reaction $Ca + Cl_2 \rightarrow CaCl_2$, what is the mole ratio of chlorine to calcium chloride?
   a. 2:3   c. 1:2
   b. 2:1   d. 1:1
   Answer: D   Difficulty: I   Section: 1   Objective: 1

5. In the reaction $N_2 + 3H_2 \rightarrow 2NH_3$, what is the mole ratio of nitrogen to ammonia?
   a. 1:1   c. 1:3
   b. 1:2   d. 2:3
   Answer: B   Difficulty: I   Section: 1   Objective: 1

6. In the reaction $2H_2 + O_2 \rightarrow 2H_2O$, what is the mole ratio of oxygen to water?
   a. 1:2   c. 8:1
   b. 2:1   d. 1:4
   Answer: A   Difficulty: I   Section: 1   Objective: 1

7. What is the mole ratio of oxygen to phosphorus(V) oxide in the reaction
   $P_4(s) + 5O_2(g) \rightarrow P_4O_{10}(s)$?
   a. 1:1   c. 5:1
   b. 1:5   d. 4:10
   Answer: C   Difficulty: I   Section: 1   Objective: 1

8. In the chemical equation $wA + xB \rightarrow yC + zD$, if one knows the mass of A and the molar masses
   of A, B, C, and D, one can determine
   a. the mass of any of the reactants or products.
   b. the mass of B only.
   c. the total mass of C and D only.
   d. the total mass of A and B only.
   Answer: A   Difficulty: I   Section: 1   Objective: 3

9. If one knows the mass and molar mass of reactant A and the molar mass of product D in a chemical reaction, one can determine the mass of product D produced by using the
   a. mole ratio of D to A from the chemical equation.
   b. group numbers of the elements of A and D in the periodic table.
   c. estimating bond energies involved in the reaction.
   d. electron configurations of the atoms in A and D.

   Answer: A   Difficulty: I   Section: 1   Objective: 3

10. What is needed to calculate the mass of ammonia gas produced from 2.0 L of nitrogen gas in excess hydrogen gas in the reaction below?

$$N_2(g) + 3H_2(g) \rightarrow 2NH_3(g)$$

   a. one molar mass and one mole ratio
   b. one molar masses and two mole ratios
   c. two molar masses, one density, and one mole ratio
   d. two densities, two molar masses, and two mole ratios

   Answer: C   Difficulty: II   Section: 1   Objective: 4

11. A chemical reaction involving substances A and B stops when B is completely used. B is the
   a. excess reactant.   c. primary reactant.
   b. limiting reactant.   d. primary product.

   Answer: B   Difficulty: II   Section: 2   Objective: 1

12. The substance that restricts the participation of other reactants in a chemical reaction is known as the
   a. limiting reactant.   c. excess reactant.
   b. limiting product.   d. excess product.

   Answer: A   Difficulty: I   Section: 2   Objective: 1

13. The substance not completely used up in a chemical reaction is known as the
   a. limiting reactant.   c. excess reactant.
   b. limiting product.   d. excess product.

   Answer: C   Difficulty: I   Section: 2   Objective: 1

14. To determine the limiting reactant in a chemical reaction, one must know the
   a. available amount of one of the reactants.
   b. amount of product formed.
   c. available amount of each reactant.
   d. speed of the reaction.

   Answer: C   Difficulty: II   Section: 2   Objective: 1

15. What is the ratio of the actual yield to the theoretical yield, multiplied by 100%?
   a. mole ratio   c. molar yield
   b. percentage yield   d. excess yield

   Answer: B   Difficulty: I   Section: 2   Objective: 2

16. What is the measured amount of a product obtained from a chemical reaction?
   a. mole ratio   c. theoretical yield
   b. percentage yield   d. actual yield

   Answer: D   Difficulty: I   Section: 2   Objective: 2

17. Actual yield must be determined by
   a. experiments.   c. theoretical yield.
   b. calculations.   d. estimation.

   Answer: A   Difficulty: I   Section: 2   Objective: 2

18. The actual yield of a chemical reaction is
   a. less than the theoretical yield.   c. equal to the percentage yield.
   b. greater than the theoretical yield.   d. greater than the percentage yield.

   Answer: A   Difficulty: I   Section: 2   Objective: 2

19. For the reaction $SO_3 + H_2O \rightarrow H_2SO_4$, calculate the percentage yield if 500. g of sulfur trioxide react with excess water to produce 575 g of sulfuric acid.
    a. 82.7%   c. 91.2%
    b. 88.3%   d. 93.9%
    Answer: D   Difficulty: II   Section: 2   Objective: 2

20. For the reaction $Cl_2 + 2KBr \rightarrow 2KCl + Br_2$, calculate the percentage yield if 200. g of chlorine react with excess potassium bromide to produce 410. g of bromine.
    a. 73.4%   c. 90.9%
    b. 82.1%   d. 98.9%
    Answer: C   Difficulty: II   Section: 2   Objective: 2

21. For the reaction $2Na + 2H_2O \rightarrow 2NaOH + H_2$, calculate the percentage yield if 80. g of water react with excess sodium to produce 4.14 g of hydrogen.
    a. 87%   c. 92%
    b. 89%   d. 98%
    Answer: C   Difficulty: II   Section: 2   Objective: 2

22. For the reaction $2Na + Cl_2 \rightarrow 2NaCl$, calculate the percentage yield if 200. g of chlorine react with excess sodium to produce 240. g of sodium chloride.
    a. 61.2%   c. 83.4%
    b. 72.8%   d. 88.4%
    Answer: B   Difficulty: II   Section: 2   Objective: 2

23. In the chemical equation $wA + xB \rightarrow yC + zD$, how many correct mole ratios can be obtained that relate only the products?
    a. 1   c. 4
    b. 2   d. 6
    Answer: B   Difficulty: II   Section: 1   Objective: 1

24. In the chemical equation $wA + xB \rightarrow yC + zD$, a comparison of the number of moles of A to the number of moles of C would be a
    a. mass ratio.   c. electron ratio.
    b. mole ratio.   d. energy proportion.
    Answer: B   Difficulty: I   Section: 1   Objective: 1

25. In the reaction, $CH_4(g) + 2O_2(g) \rightarrow CO_2(g) + 2H_2O(g)$, a mass of 25 g CO_2 is produced by reacting methane with excess oxygen. The following expression

$$25 \text{ g } CO_2 \times \frac{1 \text{ mol } CO_2}{44.01 \text{ g } CO_2} \times \frac{1 \text{ mol } CH_4}{1 \text{ mol } CO_2}$$

    calculates the
    a. mass of water produced.
    b. moles of carbon dioxide produced.
    c. minimum mass of oxygen needed.
    d. moles of methane consumed.
    Answer: D   Difficulty: II   Section: 1   Objective: 3

26. To determine the limiting reactant in a chemical reaction involving known masses of the two reactants, A and B, which of the following calculations would be the most useful?
    a. determining the masses of 100 mol A and 100 mol B
    b. finding the masses of the products
    c. calculating bond energies
    d. calculating the mass of a single product formed from each reactant
    Answer: D   Difficulty: I   Section: 2   Objective: 1

27. For the reaction $CH_4(g) + 2O_2(g) \rightarrow CO_2(g) + 2H_2O(g)$, calculate the percentage yield of carbon dioxide if 1000. g of methane react with excess oxygen to produce 2300. g of carbon dioxide.
    a. 83.88%
    b. 89.14%
    c. 92.76%
    d. 96.78%

    Answer: A   Difficulty: II   Section: 2   Objective: 2

COMPLETION

28. The branch of chemistry that deals with the numerical relationship of elements and compounds as reactants and products in a chemical reaction is known as _____.

    Answer: stoichiometry
    Difficulty: I   Section: 1   Objective: 1

29. The ratios obtained from the coefficients of substances in a balanced chemical equations are called _____ because they can be used to convert moles of one substance to moles of another substance.

    Answer: mole ratios   Difficulty: I   Section: 1   Objective: 2

30. The unit of the following expression is _____.

$$100 \, g \, H_2O \times \frac{mol \, H_2O}{18.02 \, g \ H_2O}$$

    Answer: mol H_2O Difficulty: I   Section: 1   Objective: 3

31. The unit of the following expression is _____.

$$100 \, g \, H_2O \times \frac{1}{molar \ mass \ H_2O}$$

    Answer: mol H_2O
    Difficulty: II   Section: 1   Objective: 3

32. The expression below converts the quantity, mass HCl, to the quantity, _____.

$$mass \ HCl \times \frac{1}{molar \ mass \ HCl} \times \frac{1 \, mol \, Cl_2}{2 \, mol \, HCl} \times molar \ mass \ Cl_2$$

    Answer: mass Cl_2 Difficulty: I   Section: 1   Objective: 3

33. The conversion factor $\dfrac{1}{density \ H_2O}$ can be used to find the _____ of water if you know its mass.

    Answer: volume   Difficulty: I   Section: 1   Objective: 4

34. The expression below converts the quantity, volume C_5H_{12}, to the quantity, _____.

$$volume \ C_5H_{12} \times density \ C_5H_{12} \times \frac{1}{molar \ mass \ C_5H_{12}} \times \frac{2 \, mol \, H_2}{1 \, mol \, C_5H_{12}} \times molar \ mass \ H_2$$

    Answer: mass H_2
    Difficulty: II   Section: 1   Objective: 4

35. The expression below can be used to find the _____ of 10^{16} molecules of CCl_4.

$$10^{16} \ molecules \ CCl_4 \times \frac{1 \, mol \, CCl_4}{6.022 \times 10^{23} \ molecules \ CCl_4} \times \frac{153.8 \, g \ CCl_4}{1 \, mol \, CCl_4}$$

    Answer: mass   Difficulty: II   Section: 1   Objective: 5

36. The substance that controls the quantity of product than can be formed in a chemical reaction is the _____.

    Answer: limiting reactant
    Difficulty: I   Section: 2   Objective: 1

37. The substance that is not used up completely in a chemical reaction is the _____.

    Answer: excess reactant
    Difficulty: I   Section: 2   Objective: 1

38. The measured amount of a product of a reaction is called the _____.

    Answer: actual yield
    Difficulty: I   Section: 2   Objective: 2

39. The ratio of actual yield to theoretical yield × 100% is called the _____.

    Answer: percentage yield
    Difficulty: I   Section: 2   Objective: 2

40. Almost all of the gas inside an inflated automobile safety air bag is molecular _____.

    Answer: nitrogen   Difficulty: I   Section: 3   Objective: 1

41. The function of the carburetor in a small internal combustion engine is to control the ratio of _____ to oxygen.

    Answer: fuel   Difficulty: I   Section: 3   Objective: 2

42. One of the functions of a(n) _____ is to increase the rate of the decomposition of $NO(g)$ and $NO_2(g)$ found in the exhaust gases of a car into $N_2(g)$ and $O_2(g)$.

    Answer: catalytic converter
    Difficulty: I   Section: 3   Objective: 3

43. The unit g/km is often used to express measurements of air _____ found in the exhaust gases of automobiles.

    Answer: pollutants
    Difficulty: II   Section: 3   Objective: 3

44. The proportions of the reactants and products involved in a chemical reaction are shown by the _____ in the balanced chemical equation describing the reaction.

    Answer: coefficients
    Difficulty: I   Section: 1   Objective: 1

45. On a very small scale, the numbers of particles of each substance in a reaction are represented by the _____ in the balanced chemical equation describing the reaction.

    Answer: coefficients
    Difficulty: I   Section: 1   Objective: 1

46. In the equation $N_2 + 3H_2 \rightarrow 2NH_3$, the ratio 3:2 relates mol H_2 to mol _____.
    Answer: NH_3 Difficulty: I   Section: 1   Objective: 1

47. In the equation $N_2 + 3H_2 \rightarrow 2NH_3$, the ratio 2:1 relates mol NH_3 to mol _____.
    Answer: N_2 Difficulty: I   Section: 1   Objective: 1

48. In the equation $N_2 + 3H_2 \rightarrow 2NH_3$, the mole ratio of N_2 to H_2 is _____.
    Answer: 1:3   Difficulty: I   Section: 1   Objective: 1

49. In the equation $N_2 + 3H_2 \rightarrow 2NH_3$, the mole ratio of NH_3 to N_2 is _____.
    Answer: 2:1   Difficulty: I   Section: 1   Objective: 1

50. The unit of the expression mol H_2O × molar mass H_2O is _____.
    Answer: g H_2O Difficulty: I   Section: 1   Objective: 3

51. The expression below converts the quantity, mass HCl, to the quantity, _____.

    $$\text{mass HCl} \times \frac{1}{\text{molar mass HCl}} \times \frac{1 \text{ mol } Cl_2}{2 \text{ mol HCl}}$$

    Answer: mol Cl_2 Difficulty: II   Section: 1   Objective: 3

52. Unwanted reactions that can use up reactants without making the desired products are called _____ reactions

    Answer: side   Difficulty: I   Section: 2   Objective: 1

53. If 2 moles of each reactant are available for the reaction described by the following equation, $SiO_2(s) + 3C(s) \rightarrow SiC(s) + 2CO(g)$, _____ is the substance that is the limiting reactant.

    Answer: carbon (C)
    Difficulty: I   Section: 2   Objective: 1

54. If 4 moles of each reactant are available for the reaction described by the following equation, $SiO_2(s) + 3C(s) \rightarrow SiC(s) + 2CO(g)$, _____ is the substance that is the excess reactant.

    Answer: silicon dioxide (SiO_2)
    Difficulty: I   Section: 2   Objective: 1

55. The efficiency of a reaction is described by the _____ yield.

    Answer: percentage
    Difficulty: I   Section: 2   Objective: 2

56. In an operating car engine, the least fuel-oxygen ratio should occur when the car's engine is _____.

    Answer: idling
    Difficulty: I   Section: 3   Objective: 2

57. Reactions that are started by the sun's ultraviolet light and involve nitrogen oxides emitted from car engines form _____ smog.

    Answer: photochemical
    Difficulty: I   Section: 3   Objective: 3

SHORT ANSWER

58. Explain why the conversion factor $\dfrac{3 \text{ g Mg (OH)}_2}{6 \text{ g H}_2\text{O}}$ cannot be used for the reaction $Mg_3N_2(s) + 6H_2O(l) \rightarrow 3Mg(OH)_2(aq) + 2NH_3(g)$.

    Answer:
       This conversion factor uses coefficients to compare masses directly. Ratios of moles must be used to solve stoichiometry problems.
    Difficulty: II   Section: 1   Objective: 1

59. Why must a chemical equation be balanced to solve stoichiometry problems?

    Answer:
       Only a balanced equation reveals the correct mole ratios of the reacting substances.
    Difficulty: II   Section: 1   Objective: 1

60. Why should you use moles in stoichiometry problems?

    Answer:
       The mole is used because the coefficients in the balanced equation show the number of moles of reactants and products in the chemical reaction.
    Difficulty: II   Section: 1   Objective: 2

61. Explain the difference between a limiting reactant and an excess reactant.

    Answer:
       In a reaction that goes to completion, a limiting reactant is used up, and an excess reactant is not used up.
    Difficulty: II   Section: 2   Objective: 1

62. What factor could most affect the choice of a limiting reactant for a production process?

Answer:

The most expensive chemical would probably be the limiting reactant, so it will be used up in the reaction with no excess as waste.

Difficulty: II   Section: 2   Objective: 1

63. How does the actual yield of a chemical reaction compare to the theoretical yield?

Answer:

The actual yield is always less than the theoretical yield.

Difficulty: II   Section: 2   Objective: 2

64. How is density used in stoichiometry?

Answer:

Density is used to make conversions between mass and volume. This is often important when a gas or liquid is a product or reactant.

Difficulty: I   Section: 1   Objective: 4

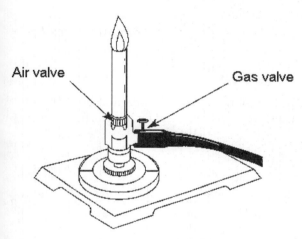

Air valve   Gas valve

65. Comparing limiting and excess reactants, explain why the flame would go out in the Bunsen burner if the indicated valves were tightened too much.

Answer:

If air is restricted, oxygen becomes the limiting reactant. If the gas is restricted, it becomes the limiting reactant. Either way, the removal of any reactant will cause the reaction to cease.

Difficulty: II   Section: 2   Objective: 2

PROBLEMS

66. How many grams of ammonium sulfate can be produced if 30.0 mol of H_2SO_4 react with excess NH_3 according to the equation $2NH_3(aq) + H_2SO_4(aq) \rightarrow (NH_4)_2SO_4(aq)$?

Answer:

$$30.0 \text{ mol } H_2SO_4 \times \frac{1 \text{ mol } (NH_4)_2SO_4}{1 \text{ mol } H_2SO_4} \times \frac{132.17 \text{ g } (NH_4)_2SO_4}{1 \text{ mol } (NH_4)_2SO_4} = 3960 \text{ g } (NH_4)_2SO_4$$

Difficulty: III   Section: 1 Objective: 3

67. What mass in grams of sodium hydroxide is produced if 20.0 g of sodium metal react with excess water according to the chemical equation
$2Na(s) + 2H_2O(l) \rightarrow 2NaOH(aq) + H_2(g)$?

Answer:

$$20.0 \text{ g Na} \times \frac{1 \text{ mol Na}}{22.99 \text{ g Na}} \times \frac{2 \text{ mol NaOH}}{2 \text{ Mol Na}} \times \frac{40.00 \text{ g NaOH}}{1 \text{ mol NaOH}} = 34.8 \text{ g NaOH}$$

Difficulty: II   Section: 1   Objective: 3

68. What volume of hydrogen gas is produced if 20.0 mol of Zn are added to excess hydrochloric acid according to the equation $Zn(s) + 2HCl(aq) \rightarrow ZnCl_2(aq) + H_2(g)$?
(Assume the density of H_2 is 0.0899 g/L)

Answer:

$$20.0 \text{ mol Zn} \times \frac{1 \text{ mol } H_2}{1 \text{ mol Zn}} \times \frac{2.02 \text{ g } H_2}{1 \text{ mol } H_2} \times \frac{1 \text{ L } H_2}{0.0899 \text{ g } H_2} = 449 \text{ L } H_2$$

Difficulty: II   Section: 1   Objective: 4

69. How many silver atoms can be produced if 0.00350 g of Cu are reacted with excess $AgNO_3$ according to the equation $Cu(s) + 2AgNO_3(aq) \rightarrow 2Ag(s) + Cu(NO_3)_2(aq)$?

Answer:

$$0.00350 \text{ g Cu} \times \frac{1 \text{ mol Cu}}{63.55 \text{ g Cu}} \times \frac{2 \text{ mol Ag}}{1 \text{ mol Cu}} \times \frac{6.022 \times 10^{23} \text{ atoms Ag}}{1 \text{ mol Ag}} = 6.63 \times 10^{19} \text{ atoms Ag}$$

Difficulty: II   Section: 1   Objective: 5

70. The reaction of 100. g of salicylic acid, $C_7H_6O_8$, with excess acetic anhydride produces 50.0 g of aspirin, $C_9H_8O_4$, according to the equation. What is the percentage yield for this reaction?
$$C_7H_6O_3 + C_4H_6O_3 \rightarrow C_9H_8O_4 + C_2H_4O_2$$

Answer:
theoretical yield:

$$100 \text{ g salicylic acid} \times \frac{1 \text{ mol salicylic acid}}{138.13 \text{ salicylic acid}} \times \frac{1 \text{ mol aspirin}}{1 \text{ mol salicylic acid}} \times \frac{180.17 \text{ g aspirin}}{1 \text{ mol aspirin}} = 130. \text{ g a}$$

$$\text{percentage yield} = \frac{50.0 \text{ g}}{130. \text{ g}} \times 100 = 38.5\%$$

Difficulty: II   Section: 2   Objective: 2

71. In the decomposition of hydrogen peroxide, the percentage yield of oxygen is 93.0%. What is the actual yield in grams of oxygen if you start with 100. g of H_2O_2? The reaction proceeds according to the equation $2H_2O_2(l) \rightarrow 2H_2O(l) + O_2(g)$.

Answer:

$$100. \text{ g } H_2O_2 \times \frac{1 \text{ mol } H_2O_2}{34.02 \text{ g } H_2O_2} \times \frac{1 \text{ mol } O_2}{2 \text{ mol } H_2O_2} \times \frac{32.00 \text{ g } O_2}{1 \text{ mol } O_2} = 47.0 \text{ g } O_2$$

$$47.0 \text{ g } O_2 \times \frac{93.0 \text{ g } O_2}{100. \text{ g } O_2} = 43.7 \text{ g } O_2$$

Difficulty: II   Section: 2   Objective: 2

72. The chemical reaction for the generation of gas in an automobile safety air bag is
$2NaN_3(s) \rightarrow 2Na(s) + 3N_2(g)$.
What volume of gas is produced if there are 130.0 grams of NaN_3 used in the reaction? (The density of nitrogen gas is 0.916 g/L.)

Answer:

$$130.0 \text{ g NaN}_3 \times \frac{1 \text{ mole NaN}_3}{(65 \text{ g NaN}_3)} \times \frac{3 \text{ moles N}_2}{(2 \text{ moles NaN}_3)} \times \frac{28 \text{ g N}_2}{1 \text{ mole N}_2} \times \frac{1 \text{ L N}_2}{(0.916 \text{ g N}_2)}$$

$$= 91.7 \text{ L N}_2$$

Difficulty: II   Section: 3   Objective: 1

73. Sulfur in gasoline can produce sulfuric acid, H2SO4, according to the two-step process shown below. For each 125 g of sulfur in gasoline, how many moles of H2SO4 will be produced?

$$S(s) + O_2(g) \rightarrow SO_2(g)$$

$$2SO_2(g) + 2H_2O(l) + O_2(g) \rightarrow 2H_2SO_4(aq)$$

Answer:

$$125 \text{ g S} \times \frac{1 \text{ mol S}}{32.07 \text{ g S}} \times \frac{1 \text{ mol SO}_2}{1 \text{ mol S}} \times \frac{2 \text{ mol H}_2\text{SO}_4}{2 \text{ mol SO}_2} = 3.90 \text{ mol H}_2\text{SO}_4$$

Difficulty: II   Section: 3   Objective: 3

ESSAY QUESTIONS

74. Describe the steps necessary to solve a mass-mass stoichiometry problem.

Answer:

Write a balanced chemical equation. Convert grams of the given substance to moles, using the molar mass. Find moles of the substance sought, using the mole ratio for the two substances in the balanced chemical equation. Convert moles of the substance sought to grams, using the molar mass.

Difficulty: I   Section: 1   Objective: 3

75. Explain the effect of limiting and excess reactants in an automobile engine that stalls.

Answer:

In a properly running engine, air and gasoline are mixed in correct proportions. When air is the limiting reactant, the engine floods with gas and will not run. When gas is the limiting reactant, the engine stalls because the amount of fuel burned is not sufficient to run the engine.

Difficulty: III   Section: 3   Objective: 2

76. The equation for the burning of gasoline shows that carbon dioxide, water, and energy are the only products, yet burning gasoline in cars causes air pollution. What information that accounts for the pollutants does the equation not reveal?

Answer:

The equation for the burning of gasoline shows only the main reaction. Products from several side reactions cause pollution. These products are carbon monoxide, nitrogen oxides, and hydrocarbons.

Difficulty: III   Section: 3   Objective: 3

Solutions Manual

Solutions for problems can also be found at go.hrw.com. Enter the keyword HW4STCTNS to obtain solutions.

Practice Problems A

1. a. Given: 1.34 mol H_2O_2
$2H_2O_2 \rightarrow 2H_2O + O_2$

Unknown: amount of O_2 in moles

mole ratio from balanced equation $= \dfrac{1 \text{ mol } O_2}{2 \text{ mol } H_2O_2}$

$\text{mol } O_2 = 1.34 \text{ mol } H_2O_2 \times \dfrac{1 \text{ mol } O_2}{1 \text{ mol } H_2O_2} = 0.670 \text{ mol } O_2$

b. Given: 1.34 mol H_2O_2
$2H_2O_2 \rightarrow 2H_2O + O_2$

Unknown: amount of H_2O

mole ratio from balanced equation $= \dfrac{2 \text{ mol } H_2O}{2 \text{ mol } H_2O_2}$

$\text{mol } H_2O = 1.34 \text{ mol } H_2O_2 \times \dfrac{2 \text{ mol } H_2O}{2 \text{ mol } H_2O_2} = 1.34 \text{ mol } H_2O$

2. a. Given: 3.30 mol Fe_2O_3
$Fe_2O_3 + 2Al \rightarrow 2Fe + Al_2O_3$

Unknown: amount of Al in moles

mole ratio from balanced equation $= \dfrac{2 \text{ mol Al}}{1 \text{ mol } Fe_2O_3}$

$\text{mol Al} = 3.30 \text{ mol } Fe_2O_3 \times \dfrac{2 \text{ mol Al}}{1 \text{ mol } Fe_2O_3} = 6.60 \text{ mol Al}$

b. Given: 3.30 mol Fe_2O_3
$Fe_2O_3 + 2Al \rightarrow 2Fe + Al_2O_3$

Unknown: amount of Fe in moles

mole ratio from balanced equation $= \dfrac{2 \text{ mol Fe}}{1 \text{ mol } Fe_2O_3}$

$\text{mol Fe} = 3.30 \text{ mol } Fe_2O_3 \times \dfrac{2 \text{ mol Fe}}{1 \text{ mol } Fe_2O_3} = 6.60 \text{ mol Fe}$

c. Given: 3.30 mol Fe_2O_3
$Fe_2O_3 + 2Al \rightarrow 2Fe + Al_2O_3$

Unknown: amount of Al_2O_3 in moles

mole ratio from balanced equation $= \dfrac{1 \text{ mol } Al_2O_3}{1 \text{ mol } Fe_2O_3}$

$\text{mol } Al_2O_3 = 3.30 \text{ mol } Fe_2O_3 \times \dfrac{1 \text{ mol } Al_2O_3}{1 \text{ mol } Fe_2O_3} = 3.30 \text{ mol } Al_2O_3$

Practice Problems B

1. Given: $Fe_2O_3 + 2Al \rightarrow 2Fe + Al_2O_3$
135 g of Fe_2O_3

Unknown: mass of Al

mole ratio from balanced equation $= \dfrac{2 \text{ mol Al}}{1 \text{ mol } Fe_2O_3}$

molar mass of $Fe_2O_3 = 2 \times \dfrac{55.85 \text{ g Fe}}{\text{mol Fe}} + 3 \times \dfrac{16.00 \text{ g O}}{\text{mol O}}$

$= 111.7 \text{ g/mol} + 48.00 \text{ g/mol} = 159.7 \text{ g/mol}$

molar mass of $Al = \dfrac{1 \times 26.98 \text{ g Al}}{\text{mol Al}} = 26.98 \text{ g/mol}$

$\text{mass Al} = 135 \text{ g } Fe_2O_3 \times \dfrac{\text{mol } Fe_2O_3}{159.7 \text{ g } Fe_2O_3} \times \dfrac{2 \text{ mol Al}}{1 \text{ mol } Fe_2O_3}$

$\times \dfrac{26.98 \text{ g Al}}{\text{mol Al}}$

$= 45.6 \text{ g Al}$

2. Given: $Fe_2O_3 + 2Al \rightarrow$
$2Fe + Al_2O_3$
23.6 Al
Unknown: mass of Al_2O_3

mole ratio from balanced equation $= \dfrac{1 \text{ mol } Al_2O_3}{2 \text{ mol } Al}$

molar mass of $Al_2O_3 = 2 \times \dfrac{26.98 \text{ g Al}}{\text{mol Al}} + 3 \times \dfrac{16.00 \text{ g O}}{\text{mol O}}$

$= 53.96 \text{ g/mol} + 48.00 \text{ g/mol} = 101.96 \text{ g/mol}$

molar mass of $Al = 1 \times \dfrac{26.98 \text{ g Al}}{\text{mol Al}} = 26.98 \text{ g/mol}$

mass $Al_2O_3 = 23.6 \text{ g Al} \times \dfrac{\text{mol Al}}{26.98 \text{ g Al}} \times \dfrac{1 \text{ mol } Al_2O_3}{2 \text{ mol Al}}$

$\times \dfrac{101.96 \text{ g } Al_2O_3}{\text{mol } Al_2O_3}$

$= 44.6 \text{ g } Al_2O_3$

3. Given: $Fe_2O_3 + 2Al \rightarrow$
$2Fe + Al_2O_3$
475 g Fe
Unknown: mass of Fe_2O_3

mole ratio from balanced equation $= \dfrac{1 \text{ mol } Fe_2O_3}{2 \text{ mol Fe}}$

molar mass of $Fe_2O_3 = 2 \times \dfrac{55.85 \text{ g Fe}}{\text{mol Fe}} + 3 \times \dfrac{16.00 \text{ g O}}{\text{mol O}}$

$= 111.7 \text{ g/mol} + 48.00 \text{ g/mol} = 159.7 \text{ g/mol}$

molar mass of $Fe = 1 \times \dfrac{55.85 \text{ g Fe}}{\text{mol Fe}} = 55.85 \text{ g/mol}$

mass $Fe_2O_3 = 475 \text{ g Fe} \times \dfrac{\text{mol Fe}}{55.85 \text{ g Fe}} \times \dfrac{1 \text{ mol } Fe_2O_3}{2 \text{ mol Fe}}$

$\times \dfrac{159.7 \text{ g } Fe_2O_3}{\text{mol } Fe_2O_3}$

$= 679 \text{ g } Fe_2O_3$

4. Given: $Fe_2O_3 + 2Al \rightarrow$
$2Fe + Al_2O_3$
Unknown: mass of Fe

mole ratio from balanced equation $= \dfrac{2 \text{ mol Fe}}{1 \text{ mol } Al_2O_3}$

molar mass of $Fe = 1 \times \dfrac{55.85 \text{ g Fe}}{\text{mol Fe}} \times 55.85 \text{ g/mol}$

molar mass of $Al_2O_3 = 2 \times \dfrac{26.98 \text{ g Al}}{\text{mol Al}} + 3 \times \dfrac{16.00 \text{ g O}}{\text{mol O}}$

$= 53.96 \text{ g/mol} + 48.00 \text{ g/mol} = 101.96 \text{ g/mol}$

mass $Fe = 97.6 \text{ g } Al_2O_3 \times \dfrac{\text{mol } Al_2O_3}{101.96 \text{ g } Al_2O_3} \times \dfrac{2 \text{ mol Fe}}{1 \text{ mol } Al_2O_3}$

$\times \dfrac{55.85 \text{ g Fe}}{\text{mol Fe}}$

$= 107 \text{ g Fe}$

Practice Problems C

1. Given: density of C_5H_{12} = 0.620 g/mL
density of C_5H_8 = 0.681 g/mL
density of H_2 = 0.0899 g/L
366 mL C_5H_{12}
$C_5H_{12} \rightarrow C_5H_8 + 2H_2$
Unknown: volume of C_5H_8

mole ratio from balanced equation = $\dfrac{1 \text{ mol } C_5H_8}{1 \text{ mol } C_5H_{12}}$

molar mass of $C_5H_8 = 5 \times \dfrac{12.01 \text{ g C}}{\text{mol C}} + 8 \times \dfrac{1.01 \text{ g H}}{\text{mol H}}$

$\qquad = 60.05 \text{ g/mol} + 8.08 \text{ g/mol} = 68.13 \text{ g/mol}$

molar mass of $C_5H_{12} = 5 \times \dfrac{12.01 \text{ g C}}{\text{mol C}} + 12 \times \dfrac{1.01 \text{ g H}}{\text{mol H}}$

$\qquad = 60.05 \text{ g/mol} + 12.1 \text{ g/mol} = 72.15 \text{ g/mol}$

mass of C_5H_{12} = 366 mL $C_5H_{12} \times \dfrac{0.620 \text{ g } C_5H_{12}}{\text{mL } C_5H_{12}}$ = 227 g C_5H_{12}

mass C_5H_8 = 227 g $C_5H_{12} \times \dfrac{\text{mol } C_5H_{12}}{72.15 \text{ g } C_5H_{12}} \times \dfrac{1 \text{ mol } C_5H_8}{1 \text{ mol } C_5H_{12}}$

$\qquad \times \dfrac{68.13 \text{ g } C_5H_8}{\text{mol } C_5H_8}$

$\qquad = 214 \text{ g } C_5H_8$

volume of C_5H_8 = 214 g $C_5H_8 \times \dfrac{\text{mL } C_5H_8}{0.681 \text{ g } C_5H_8}$ = 315 mL C_5H_8

2. Given: 4.53×10^3 mL C_5H_8
density of C_5H_{12} = 0.620 g/mL
density of C_5H_8 = 0.681 g/mL
density of H_2 = 0.0899 g/L
$C_5H_{12} \rightarrow C_5H_8 + 2H_2$
Unknown: volume of H_2

mole ratio from balanced equation = $\dfrac{2 \text{ mol } H_2}{1 \text{ mol } C_5H_8}$

molar mass of $H_2 = 2 \times \dfrac{1.01 \text{ g H}}{\text{mol H}} = 2.02 \text{ g/mol}$

molar mass of $C_5H_8 = 5 \times \dfrac{12.01 \text{ g C}}{\text{mol C}} + 8 \times \dfrac{1.01 \text{ g H}}{\text{mol H}}$

$\qquad = 60.05 \text{ g/mol} + 8.08 \text{ g/mol} = 68.13 \text{ g/mol}$

mass of C_5H_8 = $(4.53 \times 10^3$ mL $C_5H_8) \times \dfrac{0.681 \text{ g } C_5H_8}{\text{mL } C_5H_8}$

$\qquad = 3.08 \times 10^3 \text{ g } C_5H_8$

mass of H_2 = $(3.08 \times 10^3$ g $C_5H_8) \times \dfrac{\text{mol } C_5H_8}{68.13 \text{ g } C_5H_8} \times \dfrac{2 \text{ mol } H_2}{1 \text{ mol } C_5H_8}$

$\qquad \times \dfrac{2.02 \text{ g } H_2}{\text{mol } H_2}$

$\qquad = 183 \text{ g } H_2$

volume of H_2 = 183 g $H_2 \times \dfrac{\text{L } H_2}{0.0899 \text{ g/L}} = 2.03 \times 10^3 \text{ L } H_2$

3. Given: 97.3 mL C_5H_8
density of C_5H_{12} =
0.620 g/mL
density of C_5H_8 =
0.681 g/mL
density of H_2 =
0.0899 g/L
$C_5H_{12} \rightarrow C_5H_8 + 2H_2$
Unknown: volume of
C_5H_{12}

mole ratio from balanced equation $= \dfrac{1 \text{ mol } C_5H_{12}}{1 \text{ mol } C_5H_8}$

molar mass of $C_5H_{12} = 5 \times \dfrac{12.01 \text{ g C}}{\text{mol C}} + 12 \times \dfrac{1.01 \text{ g H}}{\text{mol H}}$

$$= 60.05 \text{ g/mol} + 12.1 \text{ g/mol} = 72.15 \text{ g/mol}$$

molar mass of $C_5H_8 = 5 \times \dfrac{12.01 \text{ g C}}{\text{mol C}} + 8 \times \dfrac{1.01 \text{ g H}}{\text{mol H}}$

$$= 60.05 \text{ g/mol} + 8.08 \text{ g/mol} = 68.13 \text{ g/mol}$$

mass of $C_5H_8 = 97.3 \text{ mL } C_5H_8 \times \dfrac{0.681 \text{ g } C_5H_8}{\text{mL } C_5H_8} = 66.3 \text{ g } C_5H_8$

mass of $C_5H_{12} = 66.3 \text{ g } C_5H_8 \times \dfrac{\text{mol } C_5H_8}{68.13 \text{ g } C_5H_8} \times \dfrac{1 \text{ mol } C_5H_{12}}{1 \text{ mol } C_5H_8}$

$$\times \dfrac{72.15 \text{ g } C_5H_{12}}{\text{mol } C_5H_{12}}$$

$$= 70.2 \text{ g } C_5H_{12}$$

volume of $C_5H_{12} = 70.2 \text{ g } C_5H_{12} \times \dfrac{\text{mL } C_5H_{12}}{0.620 \text{ g } C_5H_{12}} = 113 \text{ mL } C_5H_{12}$

4. Given: 1.98 $\times$
10^3 mL C_5H_{12}
density of C_5H_{12} =
0.620 g/mL
density of C_5H_8 =
0.681 g/mL
density of H_2 =
0.0899 g/L
$C_5H_{12} \rightarrow C_5H_8 + 2H_2$
Unknown: volume of H_2

mole ratio from balanced equation $= \dfrac{2 \text{ mol } H_2}{1 \text{ mol } C_5H_{12}}$

molar mass of $H_2 = 2 \times \dfrac{1.01 \text{ g H}}{\text{mol H}} = 2.02 \text{ g/mol}$

molar mass of $C_5H_{12} = 5 \times \dfrac{12.01 \text{ g C}}{\text{mol C}} + 12 \times \dfrac{1.01 \text{ g H}}{\text{mol H}}$

$$= 60.05 \text{ g/mol} + 12.1 \text{ g/mol} = 72.15 \text{ g/mol}$$

mass of $C_5H_{12} = (1.98 \times 10^3 \text{ mL } C_5H_{12}) \times \dfrac{0.620 \text{ g } C_5H_{12}}{\text{mL } C_5H_{12}}$

$$= 1.23 \times 10^3 \text{ g } C_5H_{12}$$

mass of $H_2 = (1.23 \times 10^3 \text{ g } C_5H_{12}) \times \dfrac{\text{mol } C_5H_{12}}{72.15 \text{ g } C_5H_{12}} \times \dfrac{2 \text{ mol } H_2}{1 \text{ mol } C_5H_{12}}$

$$\times \dfrac{2.02 \text{ g } H_2}{\text{mol } H_2}$$

$$= 68.9 \text{ g } H_2$$

volume of $H_2 = 68.9 \text{ g } H_2 \times \dfrac{\text{L } H_2}{0.0899 \text{ g } H_2} = 765 \text{ L } H_2$

$$= 7.65 \times 10^5 \text{ mL } H_2$$

Practice Problems D

1. Given: 384 g Br_2
$Br_2 + 5F_2 \rightarrow 2BrF_5$
Unknown: number of
molecules of
BrF_5

number of molecules of $BrF_5 = 384 \text{ g } Br_2 \times \dfrac{\text{mol } Br_2}{159.80 \text{ g } Br_2}$

$$\times \dfrac{2 \text{ mol } BrF_5}{1 \text{ mol } Br_2}$$

$$\times \dfrac{6.022 \times 10^{23} \text{ molecules } BrF_5}{\text{mol } BrF_5}$$

$$= 2.89 \times 10^{24} \text{ } BrF_5$$

2. Given: 1.11×10^{20} molecules of F_2

$Br_2 + 5F_2 \rightarrow 2BrF_5$

Unknown: number of Br_2 molecules

$(1.11 \times 10^{20} \text{ molecules } F_2) \times \dfrac{1 \text{ molecule } Br_2}{5 \text{ molecules } F_2}$

$= 2.22 \times 10^{19}$ molecules of Br_2

Section 1 Review

4. a. Given: 2.74 mol Cl_2

$Br_2 + Cl_2 \rightarrow 2BrCl$

Unknown: amount of BrCl

amount BrCl $= 2.74 \text{ mol } Cl_2 \times \dfrac{2 \text{ mol BrCl}}{1 \text{ mol } Cl_2} = 5.48$ mol BrCl

b. Given: 239.7 g Cl_2, excess Br_2

$Br_2 + Cl_2 \rightarrow 2BrCl$

Unknown: mass BrCl

mass of BrCl $= 239.7 \text{ g } Cl_2 \times \dfrac{\text{mol } Cl_2}{70.90 \text{ g } Cl_2} \times \dfrac{2 \text{ mol BrCl}}{1 \text{ mol } Cl_2}$

$\times \dfrac{115.35 \text{ g BrCl}}{\text{mol BrCl}}$

$= 780.0$ g BrCl

c. Given: density of $Br_2 =$ 3.12 g/mL

25.3 g Cl_2

$Br_2 + Cl_2 \rightarrow 2BrCl$

Unknown: volume of Br_2

volume of $Br_2 = 25.3 \text{ g } Cl_2 \times \dfrac{\text{mol } Cl_2}{70.90 \text{ g } Cl_2} \times \dfrac{1 \text{ mol } Br_2}{1 \text{ mol } Cl_2}$

$\times \dfrac{159.80 \text{ g } Br_2}{\text{mol } Br_2} \times \dfrac{\text{mL } Br_2}{3.12 \text{ g } Br_2} = 18.3$ mL Br_2

5. a. Given: 15.9 L C_2H_2 at STP

$2C_2H_2 + 5O_2 \rightarrow 4CO_2 + 2H_2O$

Unknown: volume of CO_2

volume of $CO_2 = 15.9 \text{ L } C_2H_2 \times \dfrac{1 \text{ mol } C_2H_2}{22.41 \text{ L } C_2H_2} \times \dfrac{4 \text{ mol } CO_2}{2 \text{ mol } C_2H_2}$

$\times \dfrac{22.41 \text{ L } CO_2}{\text{mol } CO_2}$

$= 31.8$ L CO_2

b. Given: density of CO_2 = 1.977 g/mL

density of $O_2 =$ 1.429 g/L

59.3 mL O_2

$2C_2H_2 + 5O_2 \rightarrow 4CO_2 + 2H_2O$

Unknown: volume CO_2

mass of $O_2 = 59.3 \text{ mL } O_2 \times \dfrac{1 \text{ L}}{1000 \text{ mL}} \times \dfrac{1.429 \text{ g } O_2}{\text{L } O_2} = 0.0847$ g O_2

volume of $CO_2 = 0.0847 \text{ g } O_2 \times \dfrac{\text{mol } O_2}{32.00 \text{ g } O_2} \times \dfrac{4 \text{ mol } CO_2}{5 \text{ mol } O_2}$

$\times \dfrac{44.01 \text{ g } CO_2}{\text{mol } CO_2} \times \dfrac{\text{mL } CO_2}{1.977 \text{ g } CO_2} = 0.0472$ mL CO_2

7. b. Given: 228 g CO_2

Unknown: mass of NaOH, LiOH

balanced equations = $2NaOH + CO_2 \rightarrow Na_2CO_3 + H_2O$

$2LiOH + CO_2 \rightarrow Li_2CO_3 + H_2O$

mass of NaOH = $228 \text{ g } CO_2 \times \dfrac{\text{mol } CO_2}{44.01 \text{ g } CO_2} \times \dfrac{2 \text{ mol NaOH}}{1 \text{ mol } CO_2}$

$\times \dfrac{40.00 \text{ g NaOH}}{\text{mol NaOH}}$

= 414 g NaOH

mass of LiOH = $228 \text{ g } CO_2 \times \dfrac{\text{mol } CO_2}{44.01 \text{ g } CO_2} \times \dfrac{2 \text{ mol LiOH}}{1 \text{ mol } CO_2}$

$\times \dfrac{23.95 \text{ g LiOH}}{\text{mol LiOH}}$

= 248 g LiOH

Practice Problems E

1. Given: 3.00 mol PCl_3
3.00 mol H_2O
$PCl_3 + 3H_2O \rightarrow$
$H_3PO_3 + 3HCl$

Unknown: excess reactant, limiting reactant, theoretical yield HCl

mass of HCl = $3.00 \text{ mol } PCl_3 \times \dfrac{3 \text{ mol HCl}}{1 \text{ mol } PCl_3} \times \dfrac{36.46 \text{ g HCl}}{\text{mol HCl}}$

= 328 g HCl

mass of HCl = $3.00 \text{ mol } H_2O \times \dfrac{3 \text{ mol HCl}}{3 \text{ mol } H_2O} \times \dfrac{36.46 \text{ g HCl}}{\text{mol HCl}}$

= 109 g HCl

Because the least amount of HCl can be formed from H_2O, H_2O is the limiting reactant. Therefore, the excess reactant is PCl_3. The theoretical yield is 109 g HCl.

2. Given: 75.0 g PCl_3
75.0 g H_2O
$PCl_3 + 3H_2O \rightarrow$
$H_3PO_3 + 3HCl$

Unknown: excess reactant, limiting reactant, theoretical yield HCl

mass HCl = $75.0 \text{ g } PCl_3 \times \dfrac{\text{mol } PCl_3}{137.32 \text{ g } PCl_3} \times \dfrac{6 \text{ mol HCl}}{2 \text{ mol } PCl_3}$

$\times \dfrac{36.46 \text{ g HCl}}{\text{mol HCl}}$

= 59.7 g HCl

mass HCl = $75.0 \text{ g } H_2O \times \dfrac{\text{mol } H_2O}{18.02 \text{ g } H_2O} \times \dfrac{6 \text{ mol HCl}}{6 \text{ mol } H_2O}$

$\times \dfrac{36.46 \text{ g HCl}}{\text{mol HCl}}$

= 152 g HCl

Because the least amount of HCl can be formed from PCl_3, PCl_3 is the limiting reactant. H_2O is the excess reactant. The theoretical yield is 59.7 g HCl.

3. Given: 1.00 mol PCl_3
50.0 g H_2O
$PCl_3 + 3H_2O \rightarrow H_3PO_3 + 3HCl$

Unknown: excess reactant, limiting reactant, theoretical yield HCl

$$\text{mass HCl} = 1.00 \text{ mol PCl}_3 \times \frac{6 \text{ mol HCl}}{2 \text{ mol PCl}_3} \times \frac{36.46 \text{ g HCl}}{\text{mol HCl}}$$

$$= 109 \text{ g HCl}$$

$$\text{mass HCl} = 50.0 \text{ g H}_2\text{O} \times \frac{\text{mol H}_2\text{O}}{18.02 \text{ g H}_2\text{O}} \times \frac{6 \text{ mol HCl}}{6 \text{ mol H}_2\text{O}}$$

$$\times \frac{36.46 \text{ g HCl}}{\text{mol HCl}}$$

$$= 101 \text{ g HCl}$$

Because the least amount of HCl can be formed from H_2O, H_2O is the limiting reactant. The excess reactant is PCl_3. The theoretical yield of HCl is 101 g.

Practice Problems F

1. Given: 14.0 g N_2
3.15 g H_2
actual yield = 14.5 g NH_3

Unknown: limiting reactant, percent yield

balanced equation = $N_2 + 3H_2 \rightarrow 2NH_3$

$$\text{mass NH}_3 = 14.0 \text{ g N}_2 \times \frac{\text{mol N}_2}{28.02 \text{ g N}_2} \times \frac{2 \text{ mol NH}_3}{1 \text{ mol N}_2} \times \frac{17.04 \text{ g NH}_3}{\text{mol NH}_3}$$

$$= 17.0 \text{ g NH}_3$$

$$\text{mass NH}_3 = 3.15 \text{ g H}_2 \times \frac{\text{mol H}_2}{2.02 \text{ g H}_2} \times \frac{2 \text{ mol NH}_3}{3 \text{ mol H}_2} \times \frac{17.04 \text{ g NH}_3}{\text{mol NH}_3}$$

$$= 17.7 \text{ g NH}_3$$

N_2 is the limiting reactant, theoretical yield = 17.0 g NH_3

$$\text{percent yield} = \frac{\text{actual yield}}{\text{theoretical yield}} \times 100$$

$$= \frac{14.5 \text{ g NH}_3}{17.0 \text{ g NH}_3} \times 100 = 85.3\%$$

2. Given: 25.5 g CH_3COOH
11.5 g C_2H_5OH
11.6 g
$CH_3COOC_2H_5$
$CH_3COOH + C_2H_5OH \rightarrow$
$CH_3COOC_2H_5 + H_2O$
Unknown: limiting
reactant,
percent yield

mass $CH_3COOC_2H_5$ = 25.5 g $CH_3COOH \times \dfrac{\text{mol } CH_3COOH}{60.06 \text{ g } CH_3COOH}$

$\times \dfrac{1 \text{ mol } CH_3COOC_2H_5}{1 \text{ mol } CH_3COOH}$

$\times \dfrac{88.12 \text{ g } CH_3COOC_2H_5}{\text{mol } CH_3COOC_2H_5}$

= 37.4 g $CH_3COOC_2H_5$

mass $CH_3COOC_2H_5$ = 11.5 g $C_2H_5OH \times \dfrac{\text{mol } C_2H_5OH}{46.08 \text{ g } C_2H_5OH}$

$\times \dfrac{1 \text{ mol } CH_3COOC_2H_5}{1 \text{ mol } C_2H_5OH}$

$\times \dfrac{88.12 \text{ g } CH_3COOC_2H_5}{\text{mol } CH_3COOC_2H_5}$

= 22.0 g $CH_3COOC_2H_5$

The limiting reactant is C_2H_5OH. The theoretical yield =
22.0 g $CH_3COOC_2H_5$

percent yield = $\dfrac{\text{actual yield}}{\text{theoretical yield}} \times 100$

$= \dfrac{17.6 \text{ g } CH_3COOC_2H_5}{22.0 \text{ g } CH_3COOC_2H_5} \times 100 = 80.0\%$

3. Given: 16.1 g Br_2
8.42 g Cl_2
21.1 g BrCl
Unknown: limiting
reactant,
percent yield

balanced equation = $Br_2 + Cl_2 \rightarrow 2BrCl$

mass BrCl = 16.1 g $Br_2 \times \dfrac{\text{mol } Br_2}{159.80 \text{ g } Br_2} \times \dfrac{2 \text{ mol BrCl}}{1 \text{ mol } Br_2}$

$\times \dfrac{115.35 \text{ g BrCl}}{\text{mol BrCl}}$

= 23.2 g BrCl

mass BrCl = 8.42 g $Cl_2 \times \dfrac{\text{mol } Cl_2}{70.90 \text{ g } Cl_2} \times \dfrac{2 \text{ mol BrCl}}{1 \text{ mol } Cl_2} \times \dfrac{115 \text{ g BrCl}}{\text{mol BrCl}}$

= 27.4 g

The limiting reactant is Br_2, the theoretical yield = 23.2 g BrCl

percent yield = $\dfrac{\text{actual yield}}{\text{theoretical yield}} \times 100$

$= \dfrac{21.1 \text{ g BrCl}}{23.2 \text{ g BrCl}} \times 100 = 90.9\%$

Practice Problems G

1. Given: percentage
yield = 85%
1.00 kg N_2
225 g H_2
$N_2 + 3H_2 \rightarrow 2NH_3$
Unknown: actual yield

$$\text{mass } NH_3 = 1.00 \text{ kg } N_2 \times \frac{1000 \text{ g } N_2}{\text{kg } N_2} \times \frac{\text{mol } N_2}{28.02 \text{ g } N_2} \times \frac{2 \text{ mol } NH_3}{1 \text{ mol } N_2}$$

$$\times \frac{17.04 \text{ g } NH_3}{\text{mol } NH_3}$$

$$= 1220 \text{ g } NH_3$$

$$\text{mass } NH_3 = 225 \text{ g } H_2 \times \frac{\text{mol } H_2}{2.02 \text{ } H_2} \times \frac{2 \text{ mol } NH_3}{3 \text{ mol } H_2} \times \frac{17.04 \text{ g } NH_3}{\text{mol } NH_3}$$

$$= 1270 \text{ g } NH_3$$

theoretical yield = 1220 g NH_3

actual yield = 1220 g $NH_3 \times 0.85 = 1.04 \times 10^3$ g NH_3

2. Given: percentage
yield = 92%
5.6×10^3 g CO
1.0×10^3 g H_2
$CO + 2H_2 \rightarrow$
$\qquad CH_3OH$
Unknown: actual yield

$$\text{mass } CH_3OH = (5.6 \times 10^3 \text{ g CO}) \times \frac{\text{mol CO}}{28.01 \text{ g CO}} \times \frac{1 \text{ mol } CH_3OH}{1 \text{ mol CO}}$$

$$\times \frac{32.05 \text{ g } CH_3OH}{\text{mol } CH_3OH}$$

$$= 6.4 \times 10^3 \text{ g } CH_3OH$$

$$\text{mass } CH_3OH = (1.0 \times 10^3 \text{ g } H_2) \times \frac{\text{mol } H_2}{2.02 \text{ g } H_2} \times \frac{1 \text{ mol } CH_3OH}{2 \text{ mol } H_2}$$

$$\times \frac{32.05 \text{ g } CH_3OH}{\text{mol } CH_3OH}$$

$$= 7.9 \times 10^3 \text{ g } CH_3OH$$

theoretical yield = 6.4×10^3 g CH_3OH

actual yield = $(6.4 \times 10^3$ g $CH_3OH) \times 0.92 = 5.9 \times 10^3$ g CH_3OH

3. Given: average
yield = 90.0%
338 g Br_2
117 g Cl_2
Unknown: actual yield

balanced equation = $Br_2 + Cl_2 \rightarrow 2BrCl$

$$\text{mass BrCl} = 338 \text{ g } Br_2 \times \frac{\text{mol } Br_2}{159.80 \text{ g } Br_2} \times \frac{2 \text{ mol BrCl}}{1 \text{ mol } Br_2}$$

$$\times \frac{115.35 \text{ g BrCl}}{\text{mol BrCl}}$$

$$= 488 \text{ g BrCl}$$

$$\text{mass BrCl} = 117 \text{ g } Cl_2 \times \frac{\text{mol } Cl_2}{70.90 \text{ g } Cl_2} \times \frac{2 \text{ mol BrCl}}{1 \text{ mol } Cl_2}$$

$$\times \frac{115.35 \text{ g BrCl}}{\text{mol BrCl}}$$

$$= 576 \text{ g BrCl}$$

theoretical yield = 488 g BrCl

actual yield = 488 g BrCl $\times 0.900 = 439$ g BrCl

Section 2 Review

6. Given: 8.85 g Fe
0.27 g H_2
excess HCl

Unknown: theoretical
yield, percent
yield H_2

balanced equation = $Fe + 2HCl \rightarrow H_2 + FeCl_2$

theoretical yield of H_2 = 8.85 g Fe $\times \dfrac{mol\ Fe}{55.85\ g\ Fe} \times \dfrac{1\ mol\ H_2}{1\ mol\ Fe}$

$$\times \dfrac{2.02\ g\ H_2}{mol\ H_2}$$

$$= 0.32\ g\ H_2$$

percent yield = $\dfrac{actual\ yield}{theoretical\ yield} \times 100$

$$= \dfrac{0.27\ g\ H_2}{0.32\ g\ H_2} \times 100 = 84\%$$

7. b. Given: 100.0 g P_4H_{10}
200.0 g H_2O

Unknown: theoretical
yield

balanced equation = $P_4H_{10} + 6H_2O \rightarrow 4H_3PO_4$

mass H_3PO_4 = 100.0 g $P_4H_{10} \times \dfrac{mol\ P_4H_{10}}{283.88\ g\ P_4H_{10}} \times \dfrac{4\ mol\ H_3PO_4}{1\ mol\ P_4H_{10}}$

$$\times \dfrac{98.00\ g\ H_3PO_4}{mol\ H_3PO_4}$$

$$= 138.1\ g\ H_3PO_4$$

mass H_3PO_4 = 200.0 g $H_2O \times \dfrac{mol\ H_2O}{18.02\ g\ H_2O} \times \dfrac{4\ mol\ H_3PO_4}{6\ mol\ H_2O}$

$$\times \dfrac{98.00\ H_3PO_4}{mol\ H_3PO_4}$$

$$= 725.1\ g\ H_3PO_4$$

theoretical yield = 138.1 g H_3PO_4

c. Given: 126.2 g H_3PO_4

Unknown: percent
yield

percent yield = $\dfrac{actual\ yield}{theoretical\ yield} \times 100$

$$= \dfrac{126.2\ g\ H_3PO_4}{138.1\ g\ H_3PO_4} \times 100 = 91.38\%$$

8. Given: 3.5 mol $TiCl_4$
4.5 mol O_2
$TiCl_4 + O_2 \rightarrow$
$TiO_2 + 2Cl_2$

Unknown: limiting reac-
tant, amount
of products,
amount of
excess reactant
remaining

mass TiO_2 = 3.5 mol $TiCl_4 \times \dfrac{1\ mol\ TiO_2}{1\ mol\ TiCl_4} \times \dfrac{79.90\ g\ TiO_2}{mol\ TiO_2}$

$$= 280\ g\ TiO_2$$

mass TiO_2 = 4.5 mol $O_2 \times \dfrac{1\ mol\ TiO_2}{1\ mol\ O_2} \times \dfrac{79.90\ g\ TiO_2}{mol\ TiO_2}$

$$= 360\ g\ TiO_2$$

Therefore, the limiting reactant is $TiCl_4$.

amount TiO_2 = 3.5 mol

amount Cl_2 = 2(3.5 mol) = 7.0 mol

amount O_2 remaining = 4.5 mol − 3.5 mol = 1.0 mol O_2

9. Given: 1.85 g Al
percent yield = 56.6%
Al(s) + CuSO$_4$(aq) →
Cu(s) + Al$_2$(SO$_4$)$_3$(aq)

Unknown: mass of Cu

balanced equation = 2Al(s) + 3CuSO$_4$(aq) → 3Cu(s) + Al$_2$(SO$_4$)$_3$(aq)

theoretical yield of Cu = 1.85 g Al $\times \dfrac{\text{mol Al}}{26.98 \text{ g Al}} \times \dfrac{3 \text{ mol Cu}}{2 \text{ mol Al}}$

$\times \dfrac{63.55 \text{ g Cu}}{\text{mol Cu}}$

= 6.54 g Cu

actual yield = 6.54 g Cu × 0.566 = 3.70 g Cu

10. Given: 2.00 × 10^3 g CaCO$_3$
1.05 × 10^3 g CaO
CaCO$_3$(s) →
CaO(s) + CO$_2$(g)

Unknown: percent yield

theoretical yield of CaO = (2.00 × 10^3 g CaCO$_3$) $\times \dfrac{\text{mol CaCO}_3}{100.09 \text{ g CaCO}_3}$

$\times \dfrac{1 \text{ mol CaO}}{1 \text{ mol CaCO}_3} \times \dfrac{56.08 \text{ g CaO}}{\text{mol CaO}}$

= 1.12 × 10^3 g CaO

percent yield = $\dfrac{\text{actual yield}}{\text{theoretical yield}} \times 100$

= $\dfrac{1.05 \times 10^3 \text{ g CaO}}{1.12 \times 10^3 \text{ g CaO}} \times 100 = 93.8\%$

11. b. Given: 10.1 g Mg
excess H$_2$O
21.0 g Mg(OH$_2$)

Unknown: percent yield

balanced equation = Mg + 2H$_2$O → Mg(OH)$_2$ + H$_2$

theoretical yield = 10.1 g Mg $\times \dfrac{\text{mol Mg}}{24.31 \text{ g Mg}} \times \dfrac{1 \text{ mol Mg(OH)}_2}{1 \text{ mol Mg}}$

$\times \dfrac{58.33 \text{ g Mg(OH)}_2}{\text{mol Mg(OH)}_2}$

= 24.2 g Mg(OH)$_2$

percent yield = $\dfrac{\text{actual yield}}{\text{theoretical yield}} \times 100$

= $\dfrac{21.0 \text{ g Mg(OH)}_2}{24.2 \text{ g Mg(OH)}_2} \times 100 = 86.8\%$

c. Given: 24 g Mg
percent yield = 95%

Unknown: mass of Mg(OH)$_2$

theoretical yield = 24 g Mg $\times \dfrac{\text{mol Mg}}{24.31 \text{ g Mg}} \times \dfrac{1 \text{ mol Mg(OH)}_2}{1 \text{ mol Mg(OH)}_2}$

$\times \dfrac{58.33 \text{ g Mg(OH)}_2}{\text{mol Mg(OH)}_2}$

= 58 g Mg(OH)$_2$

actual yield = 58 g Mg(OH)$_2$ × 0.95 = 55 g Mg(OH)$_2$

12. a. Given: 19.9 g CuO
2.02 g H$_2$
CuO(s) + H$_2$(g) →
Cu(s) + H$_2$O(g)

Unknown: limiting reactant

mass Cu = 19.9 g CuO $\times \dfrac{\text{mol CuO}}{79.55 \text{ g CuO}} \times \dfrac{1 \text{ mol Cu}}{1 \text{ mol CuO}} \times \dfrac{63.55 \text{ g Cu}}{\text{mol Cu}}$

= 15.9 g Cu

mass Cu = 2.02 g H$_2$ $\times \dfrac{\text{mol H}_2}{2.02 \text{ g H}_2} \times \dfrac{1 \text{ mol Cu}}{1 \text{ mol H}_2} \times \dfrac{63.55 \text{ g Cu}}{\text{mol Cu}}$

= 63.6 g Cu

Therefore, the limiting reactant is CuO.

Solutions Manual *continued*

b. Given: actual yield = 15.0 g Cu

Unknown: percent yield

$$\text{percent yield} = \frac{\text{actual yield}}{\text{theoretical yield}} \times 100$$

$$= \frac{15.0 \text{ g Cu}}{15.9 \text{ g Cu}} \times 100 = 94.3\%$$

c. Given: 20.6 g CuO
excess H_2
percent yield = 91%

Unknown: mass of Cu

$$\text{theoretical yield} = 20.6 \text{ g CuO} \times \frac{\text{mol CuO}}{79.55 \text{ g CuO}} \times \frac{1 \text{ mol Cu}}{1 \text{ mol CuO}}$$

$$\times \frac{63.55 \text{ g Cu}}{\text{mol Cu}}$$

$$= 16.5 \text{ g Cu}$$

$$\text{actual yield} = 16.5 \text{ g Cu} \times 0.91 = 15.0 \text{ g Cu}$$

---

13. Given: 20 mol H_2
20 mol O_2

Unknown: amount of each remaining

balanced equation = $2H_2 + O_2 \rightarrow 2H_2O$

$$\text{mass } H_2O = 20 \text{ mol } H_2 \times \frac{2 \text{ mol } H_2O}{2 \text{ mol } H_2} \times \frac{18.02 \text{ g } H_2O}{\text{mol } H_2O}$$

$$= 360 \text{ g } H_2O$$

$$\text{mass } H_2O = 20 \text{ mol } O_2 \times \frac{2 \text{ mol } H_2O}{1 \text{ mol } O_2} \times \frac{18.02 \text{ g } H_2O}{\text{mol } H_2O}$$

$$= 720 \text{ g } H_2O$$

Since H_2 is the limiting reactant, 0 moles of H_2 remain.

amount of O_2 remaining = 20 moles − 10 moles = 10 moles

amount of H_2O = 20 moles

---

14. Given: 27 g CaO
41 g $CaCO_3$

Unknown: percent yield, is it reasonable?

balanced equation = $CaCO_3 \rightarrow CaO + CO_2$

$$\text{theoretical yield CaO} = 41 \text{ g } CaCO_3 \times \frac{\text{mol } CaCO_3}{100.09 \text{ g } CaCO_3}$$

$$\times \frac{1 \text{ mol CaO}}{1 \text{ mol } CaCO_3} \times \frac{56.08 \text{ g CaO}}{\text{mol CaO}}$$

$$= 23 \text{ g CaO}$$

$$\text{percent yield} = \frac{\text{actual yield}}{\text{theoretical yield}} \times 100$$

$$= \frac{27 \text{ g CaO}}{23 \text{ g CaO}} \times 100 = 120\%, \text{ this is not reasonable.}$$

Practice Problems H

1. Given: 93 g NaN_3

Unknown: mass of Na

$2NaN_3(s) \rightarrow 2Na(s) + 3N_2(g)$

$$\text{mass Na} = 93 \text{ g } NaN_3 \times \frac{\text{mol } NaN_3}{65.02 \text{ g } NaN_3} \times \frac{2 \text{ mol Na}}{2 \text{ mol } NaN_3}$$

$$\times \frac{22.99 \text{ g Na}}{\text{mol Na}}$$

$$= 33 \text{ g Na}$$

2. Given: 35.3 g Na

$6Na(s) + Fe_2O_3(s) \rightarrow$
$3Na_2O(s) + 2Fe(s)$

Unknown: mass of Fe_2O_3

$$\text{mass } Fe_2O_3 = 35.3 \text{ g Na} \times \frac{\text{mol Na}}{22.99 \text{ g Na}} \times \frac{1 \text{ mol } Fe_2O_3}{6 \text{ mol Na}}$$

$$\times \frac{159.70 \text{ g } Fe_2O_3}{\text{mol } Fe_2O_3}$$

$$= 40.9 \text{ g } Fe_2O_3$$

3. Given: 44.7 g Na_2O

density of $NaHCO_3$
$= 2.20 \text{ g/mL}$

$Na_2O(s) + 2CO_2(g) +$
$H_2O(g) \rightarrow 2NaHCO_3(s)$

Unknown: volume of
$NaHCO_3$

$$\text{mass } NaHCO_3 = 44.7 \text{ g } Na_2O \times \frac{\text{mol } Na_2O}{61.98 \text{ g } Na_2O} \times \frac{2 \text{ mol } NaHCO_3}{1 \text{ mol } Na_2O}$$

$$\times \frac{84.01 \text{ g } NaHCO_3}{\text{mol } NaHCO_3}$$

$$= 122 \text{ g } NaHCO_3$$

4. a. Given: 65.1 L CO_2

density of CO_2
$= 1.35 \text{ g/L}$

$NaHCO_3 + HC_2H_3O_2 \rightarrow$
$NaC_2H_3O_2 + CO_2 + H_2O$

Unknown: mass
$NaHCO_3$

$$\text{mass } CO_2 = 65.1 \text{ L } CO_2 \times 1.35 \text{ g/L } CO_2 = 87.9 \text{ g } CO_2$$

$$\text{mass } NaHCO_3 = 87.9 \text{ g } CO_2 \times \frac{\text{mol } CO_2}{44.01 \text{ g } CO_2} \times \frac{1 \text{ mol } NaHCO_3}{1 \text{ mol } CO_2}$$

$$\times \frac{84.01 \text{ g } NaHCO_3}{\text{mol } NaHCO_3}$$

$$= 168 \text{ g } NaHCO_3$$

b. Unknown: mass of
$HC_2H_3O_2$

$$\text{mass } HC_2H_3O_2 = 87.9 \text{ g } CO_2 \times \frac{\text{mol } CO_2}{44.01 \text{ g } CO_2} \times \frac{1 \text{ mol } HC_2H_3O_2}{1 \text{ mol } CO_2}$$

$$\times \frac{60.06 \text{ g } HC_2H_3O_2}{\text{mol } HC_2H_3O_2}$$

$$= 1.20 \times 10^2 \text{ g } HC_2H_3O_2$$

Practice Problems I

1. Given: volume of cylinder
$= 5.00 \times 10^2 \text{ cm}^3$

1.00 mL of
isooctane

1 cycle = firing of
8 cylinders

air is 21% O_2 by
volume

$2C_8H_{18} + 25O_2 \rightarrow$
$16CO_2 + 18H_2O$

density of
isooctane =
0.692 g/mL

density of O_2 =
1.33 g/L

Unknown: number of
cycles

$$1.00 \text{ mL } C_8H_{18} \times \frac{0.692 \text{ g } C_8H_{18}}{1 \text{ mL } C_8H_{18}} \times \frac{1 \text{ mol } C_8H_{18}}{114.26 \text{ g } C_8H_{18}} \times \frac{25 \text{ mol } O_2}{2 \text{ mol } C_8H_{18}}$$

$$\times \frac{32.00 \text{ g } O_2}{1 \text{ mol } O_2} \times \frac{1 \text{ L } O_2}{1.33 \text{ g } O_2} = 1.82 \text{ L } O_2$$

$$= 1.82 \times 10^3 \text{ mL } O_2 = 1.82 \times 10^3 \text{ cm}^3 O_2$$

$$1.82 \times 10^3 \text{ cm}^3 O_2 \times \frac{1 \text{ cylinder}}{5.00 \times 10^2 \text{ cm}^3 \text{ air}} \times \frac{1 \text{ cycle}}{8 \text{ cylinders}}$$

$$\times \frac{1 \text{ volume air}}{0.21 \text{ volume } O_2} = 2.17 \text{ cycles}$$

2. Given: volume of cylinder
$= 5.00 \times 10^2$ cm^3
25.0 cycles
1 cycle = firing of
6 cylinders
air is 21% O_2 by
volume
$2C_8H_{18} + 25O_2 \rightarrow$
$16CO_2 + 18H_2O$
density of
isooctane =
0.692 g/mL
density of O_2 =
1.33 g/L

Unknown: mL of
isooctane

$$25.0 \text{ cycles} \times \frac{6 \text{ cylinders}}{\text{cycle}} \times \frac{5.00 \times 10^2 \text{ cm}^3 \text{ air}}{1 \text{ cylinder}} \times \frac{0.21 \text{ cm}^3 \text{ O}_2}{1.00 \text{ cm}^3 \text{ air}}$$

$$\times \frac{1 \text{ mL}}{1 \text{ cm}^3} \times \frac{1 \text{ L}}{1000 \text{ mL}} \times \frac{1.33 \text{ g O}_2}{1 \text{ L O}_2} \times \frac{1 \text{ mol O}_2}{32.00 \text{ g O}_2}$$

$$\times \frac{2 \text{ mol C}_8\text{H}_{18}}{25 \text{ mol O}_2} \times \frac{114.26 \text{ g C}_8\text{H}_{18}}{1 \text{ mol C}_8\text{H}_{18}} \times \frac{1 \text{ mL C}_8\text{H}_{18}}{0.692 \text{ g C}_8\text{H}_{18}}$$

$$= 8.64 \text{ mL C}_8\text{H}_{18}$$

3. Given: density of CH_3OH
= 0.79 g/mL
51.0 mL CH_3OH
air is 21% O_2 by
volume
density of O_2 =
1.33 g/L

Unknown: volume of air
needed

$$2CH_3OH + 3O_2 \rightarrow 2CO_2 + 4H_2O$$

$$51.0 \text{ mL CH}_3\text{OH} \times \frac{0.79 \text{ g CH}_3\text{OH}}{1 \text{ mL CH}_3\text{OH}} \times \frac{1 \text{ mol CH}_3\text{OH}}{32.05 \text{ g CH}_3\text{OH}}$$

$$\times \frac{3 \text{ mol O}_2}{2 \text{ mol CH}_3\text{OH}} \times \frac{32 \text{ g O}_2}{1 \text{ mol O}_2} \times \frac{1 \text{ L O}_2}{1.33 \text{ g O}_2}$$

$$\times \frac{1.00 \text{ L air}}{0.21 \text{ L O}_2} = 2.2 \times 10^2 \text{ L air}$$

Practice Problems J

1. Given: 2.55 g CO
Unknown: mass of CO_2

$$2CO + O_2 \rightarrow 2CO_2$$

$$\text{mass CO}_2 = 2.55 \text{ g CO} \times \frac{\text{mol CO}}{28.01 \text{ g CO}} \times \frac{2 \text{ mol CO}_2}{2 \text{ mol CO}} \times \frac{44.01 \text{ g CO}_2}{\text{mol CO}_2}$$

$$= 4.01 \text{ g CO}_2$$

Section 3 Review

5. Given: 22.4 g NaN_3
Unknown: mass of Na_2O

$$2NaN_3 \rightarrow 2Na + 3N_2$$

$$6Na + Fe_2O_3 \rightarrow 3Na_2O + 2Fe$$

$$\text{mass Na} = 22.4 \text{ g NaN}_3 \times \frac{\text{mol NaN}_3}{65.02 \text{ g NaN}_3} \times \frac{2 \text{ mol Na}}{2 \text{ mol NaN}_3}$$

$$\times \frac{22.99 \text{ g Na}}{\text{mol Na}}$$

$$= 7.92 \text{ g Na}$$

$$\text{mass Na}_2\text{O} = 7.92 \text{ g Na} \times \frac{\text{mol Na}}{22.99 \text{ g Na}} \times \frac{3 \text{ mol Na}_2\text{O}}{6 \text{ mol Na}}$$

$$\times \frac{61.98 \text{ g Na}_2\text{O}}{\text{mol Na}_2\text{O}}$$

$$= 10.7 \text{ g Na}_2\text{O}$$

6. Given: 44.4 g Na_2O

Unknown: mass $NaHCO_3$

$$Na_2O + 2CO_2 + H_2O \rightarrow 2NaHCO_3$$

$$\text{mass } NaHCO_3 = 44.4 \text{ g } Na_2O \times \frac{\text{mol } Na_2O}{61.98 \text{ g } Na_2O} \times \frac{2 \text{ mol } NaHCO_3}{1 \text{ mol } Na_2O}$$

$$\times \frac{84.01 \text{ g } NaHCO_3}{\text{mol } NaHCO_3}$$

$$= 120 \text{ g } NaHCO_3$$

Chapter Review

27. a. Given: 3.3 mol O_2

$$2H_2 + O_2 \rightarrow 2H_2O$$

Unknown: amount H_2

$$\text{amount } H_2 = 3.3 \text{ mol } O_2 \times \frac{2 \text{ mol } H_2}{1 \text{ mol } O_2} = 6.6 \text{ mol } H_2$$

b. Given: 6.72 mol H_2O

Unknown: amount O_2

$$\text{amount } O_2 = 6.72 \text{ mol } H_2O \times \frac{1 \text{ mol } O_2}{2 \text{ mol } H_2O} = 3.36 \text{ mol } O_2$$

c. Given: 8.12 mol H_2O

Unknown: amount H_2

$$\text{amount } H_2 = 8.12 \text{ mol } H_2 \times \frac{2 \text{ mol } H_2O}{2 \text{ mol } H_2} = 8.12 \text{ mol } H_2$$

28. a. Given:

$$2N_2H_4 + N_2O_4 \rightarrow$$
$$3N_2 + 4H_2O$$
$$1.22 \times 10^3 \text{ mol } N_2$$

Unknown: amount H_2O

$$\text{amount } H_2O = (1.22 \times 10^3 \text{ mol } N_2) \times \frac{4 \text{ mol } H_2O}{3 \text{ mol } N_2}$$

$$= 1.63 \times 10^3 \text{ mol } H_2O$$

b. Given: $1.45 \times 10^3 \text{ mol } N_2O_4$

Unknown: amount N_2H_4

$$\text{amount } N_2H_4 = (1.45 \times 10^3 \text{ mol } N_2O_4) \times \frac{2 \text{ mol } N_2H_4}{1 \text{ mol } N_2O_4}$$

$$= 2.90 \times 10^3 \text{ mol } N_2H_4$$

c. Given: $2.13 \times 10^3 \text{ mol } N_2O_4$

Unknown: amount N_2

$$\text{amount } N_2 = (2.13 \times 10^3 \text{ mol } N_2O_4) \times \frac{3 \text{ mol } N_2}{1 \text{ mol } N_2O_4}$$

$$= 6.39 \times 10^3 \text{ mol } N_2$$

29. a. Given: 1.44 mol Al

Unknown: amount O_2

$$4Al + 3O_2 \rightarrow 2Al_2O_3$$

$$\text{amount } O_2 = 1.44 \text{ mol } Al \times \frac{3 \text{ mol } O_2}{4 \text{ mol } Al} = 1.08 \text{ mol } O_2$$

b. Given: 5.23 mol Al

Unknown: amount Al_2O_3

$$\text{amount } Al_2O_3 = 5.23 \text{ mol } Al \times \frac{2 \text{ mol } Al_2O_3}{4 \text{ mol } Al} = 2.62 \text{ mol } Al_2O_3$$

c. Given: 2.98 mol O_2

Unknown: amount Al_2O_3

$$\text{amount } Al_2O_3 = 2.98 \text{ mol } O_2 \times \frac{2 \text{ mol } Al_2O_3}{3 \text{ mol } O_2} = 1.99 \text{ mol } Al_2O_3$$

30. a. Given: 485 g CaC_2
$$CaC_2(s) + 2H_2O(l) \rightarrow$$
$$C_2H_2(g) + Ca(OH)_2(s)$$
Unknown: mass H_2O

mass H_2O = 485 g $CaC_2 \times \dfrac{\text{mol } CaC_2}{64.10 \text{ g } CaC_2} \times \dfrac{2 \text{ mol } H_2O}{1 \text{ mol } CaC_2}$

$$\times \dfrac{18.02 \text{ g } H_2O}{\text{mol } H_2O}$$

$$= 273 \text{ g } H_2O$$

b. Given: 23.6 g C_2H_2
Unknown: mass CaC_2

mass CaC_2 = 23.6 g $C_2H_2 \times \dfrac{\text{mol } C_2H_2}{26.04 \text{ g } C_2H_2} \times \dfrac{1 \text{ mol } CaC_2}{1 \text{ mol } C_2H_2}$

$$\times \dfrac{64.10 \text{ g } CaC_2}{\text{mol } CaC_2}$$

$$= 58.1 \text{ g } CaC_2$$

c. Given: 55.3 g $Ca(OH)_2$
Unknown: mass H_2O

mass H_2O = 55.3 g $Ca(OH)_2 \times \dfrac{\text{mol } Ca(OH)_2}{74.10 \text{ g } Ca(OH)_2} \times \dfrac{2 \text{ mol } H_2O}{1 \text{ mol } Ca(OH)_2}$

$$\times \dfrac{18.02 \text{ g } H_2O}{\text{mol } H_2O}$$

$$= 26.9 \text{ g } H_2O$$

31. a. Given: 125 g $KClO_3$
$$2KClO_3(s) \rightarrow 2KCl(s) + 3O_2(g)$$
Unknown: mass O_2

mass O_2 = 125 g $KClO_3 \times \dfrac{\text{mol } KClO_3}{122.55 \text{ g } KClO_3} \times \dfrac{3 \text{ mol } O_2}{2 \text{ mol } KClO_3}$

$$\times \dfrac{32.00 \text{ g } O_2}{\text{mol } O_2}$$

$$= 49.0 \text{ g } O_2$$

b. Given: 293 g O_2
Unknown: mass
$KClO_3$

mass $KClO_3$ = 293 g $O_2 \times \dfrac{\text{mol } O_2}{32.00 \text{ g } O_2} \times \dfrac{2 \text{ mol } KClO_3}{3 \text{ mol } O_2}$

$$\times \dfrac{122.55 \text{ g } KClO_3}{\text{mol } KClO_3}$$

$$= 748 \text{ g } KClO_3$$

c. Given: 20.8 g $KClO_3$
Unknown: mass KCl

mass KCl = 20.8 g $KClO_3 \times \dfrac{\text{mol } KClO_3}{122.55 \text{ g } KClO_3} \times \dfrac{2 \text{ mol } KCl}{2 \text{ mol } KClO_3}$

$$\times \dfrac{74.55 \text{ g KCl}}{\text{mol KCl}}$$

$$= 12.7 \text{ g KCl}$$

32. Given: 38.8 g Al
Unknown: mass Al_2O_3

balanced equation = $4Al + 3O_2 \rightarrow 2Al_2O_3$

mass Al_2O_3 = 38.8 g Al $\times \dfrac{\text{mol Al}}{26.98 \text{ g Al}} \times \dfrac{2 \text{ mol } Al_2O_3}{4 \text{ mol Al}}$

$$\times \dfrac{101.96 \text{ g } Al_2O_3}{\text{mol } Al_2O_3}$$

$$= 73.3 \text{ g } Al_2O_3$$

33. Given: 2.22 mol O_3
Unknown: mass O_2

balanced equation = $2O_3 \rightarrow 3O_2$

mass O_2 = 2.22 mol $O_3 \times \dfrac{3 \text{ mol } O_2}{2 \text{ mol } O_3} \times \dfrac{32.00 \text{ } O_2}{\text{mol } O_2} = 107 \text{ g } O_2$

34. a. Given: density O_2 = 1.428 g/L

$2KClO_3(s) \rightarrow 2KCl(s) + 3O_2(g)$

5.00×10^{-2} mol $KClO_3$

Unknown: volume O_2

$$\text{volume } O_2 = (5.00 \times 10^{-2} \text{ mol } KClO_3) \times \frac{3 \text{ mol } O_2}{2 \text{ mol } KClO_3} \times \frac{32.00 \text{ g } O_2}{\text{mol } O_2}$$

$$\times \frac{L\ O_2}{1.428 \text{ g } O_2} = 1.68 \text{ L } O_2$$

b. Given: 42.0 mL O_2

Unknown: mass $KClO_3$

$$\text{mass } O_2 = 42.0 \text{ mL } O_2 \times \frac{1 \text{ L } O_2}{1000 \text{ mL } O_2} \times \frac{1.428 \text{ g } O_2}{L\ O_2} = 0.0600 \text{ g } O_2$$

$$\text{mass } KClO_3 = 0.0600 \text{ g } O_2 \times \frac{\text{mol } O_2}{32.00 \text{ g } O_2} \times \frac{2 \text{ mol } KClO_3}{3 \text{ mol } O_2}$$

$$\times \frac{122.55 \text{ g } KClO_3}{\text{mol } KClO_3}$$

$$= 0.153 \text{ g } KClO_3$$

c. Given: 55.2 g $KClO_3$

Unknown: volume O_2

$$\text{volume } O_2 = 55.2 \text{ g } KClO_3 \times \frac{\text{mol } KClO_3}{122.55 \text{ g } KClO_3} \times \frac{3 \text{ mol } O_2}{2 \text{ mol } KClO_3}$$

$$\times \frac{32.00 \text{ g } O_2}{\text{mol } O_2} \times \frac{L\ O_2}{1.428 \text{ g } O_2} = 15.1 \text{ L } O_2 = 1.51 \times 10^4 \text{ mL } O_2$$

---

35. a. Given: 342 g H_2O_2

density of O_2 = 1.428 g/L

Unknown: volume O_2

balanced equation = $2H_2O_2 \rightarrow 2H_2O + O_2$

$$\text{volume } O_2 = 342 \text{ g } H_2O_2 \times \frac{\text{mol } H_2O_2}{34.02\ H_2O_2} \times \frac{1 \text{ mol } O_2}{2 \text{ mol } H_2O_2}$$

$$\times \frac{32.00 \text{ g } O_2}{\text{mol } O_2} \times \frac{L\ O_2}{1.428 \text{ g } O_2} = 113 \text{ L } O_2$$

b. Given: density of H_2O_2 = 1.407 g/mL

55 mL H_2O_2

Unknown: volume O_2

$$\text{mass } H_2O_2 = 55 \text{ mL } H_2O_2 \times \frac{1.407 \text{ g } H_2O_2}{\text{mL } H_2O_2} = 77 \text{ g } H_2O_2$$

$$\text{volume } O_2 = 77 \text{ g } H_2O_2 \times \frac{\text{mol } H_2O_2}{34.02 \text{ g } H_2O_2} \times \frac{1 \text{ mol } O_2}{2 \text{ mol } H_2O_2}$$

$$\times \frac{32.00 \text{ g } O_2}{\text{mol } O_2} \times \frac{L\ O_2}{1.428 \text{ g } O_2} = 25 \text{ L } O_2$$

c. Given: 22.5 g H_2O_2

Unknown: volume O_2

$$\text{volume } O_2 = 22.5 \text{ g } H_2O_2 \times \frac{\text{mol } H_2O_2}{34.02 \text{ g } H_2O_2} \times \frac{1 \text{ mol } O_2}{2 \text{ mol } H_2O_2}$$

$$\times \frac{32.00 \text{ g } O_2}{\text{mol } O_2} \times \frac{L\ O_2}{1.428 \text{ g } O_2} = 7.41 \text{ L } O_2$$

---

36. a. Given: 1.11 mol O_2

$2NO + O_2 \rightarrow 2NO_2$

Unknown: number of molecules of NO_2

$$\text{number of molecules } NO_2 = 1.11 \text{ mol } O_2 \times \frac{2 \text{ mol } NO_2}{1 \text{ mol } O_2}$$

$$\times \frac{6.022 \times 10^{23} \text{ molecules } NO_2}{\text{mol } NO_2}$$

$$= 1.34 \times 10^{24} \text{ molecules } NO_2$$

b. Given: 25.7 g O_2

Unknown: number of molecules of NO

$$\text{number of molecules } NO = 25.7 \text{ g } O_2 \times \frac{\text{mol } O_2}{32.00 \text{ g } O_2} \times \frac{2 \text{ mol } NO}{1 \text{ mol } O_2}$$

$$\times \frac{6.022 \times 10^{23} \text{ molecules } NO}{\text{mol } NO}$$

$$= 9.67 \times 10^{23} \text{ molecules } NO$$

Solutions Manual *continued*

c. Given: 3.76×10^{22} molecules NO_2

Unknown: number of molecules of O_2

number of molecules $O_2 = (3.76 \times 10^{22}$ molecules $NO_2)$

$$\times \frac{1 \text{ molecule } O_2}{2 \text{ molecules } NO_2}$$

$$= 1.88 \times 10^{22} \text{ molecules } O_2$$

---

37. a. Given: 27.6 g H_2O

$2Na + 2H_2O \rightarrow 2NaOH + H_2$

Unknown: number of molecules of H_2

number of molecules $H_2 = 27.6$ g $H_2O \times \dfrac{\text{mol } H_2O}{18.02 \text{ g } H_2O} \times \dfrac{1 \text{ mol } H_2}{2 \text{ mol } H_2O}$

$$\times \frac{6.022 \times 10^{23} \text{ molecules } H_2}{\text{mol } H_2}$$

$$= 4.61 \times 10^{23} \text{ molecules } H_2$$

b. Given: 12.9 g H_2O

Unknown: number of Na atoms

number of Na atoms $= 12.9$ g $H_2O \times \dfrac{\text{mol } H_2O}{18.02 \text{ g } H_2O} \times \dfrac{2 \text{ mol } Na}{2 \text{ mol } H_2O}$

$$\times \frac{6.022 \times 10^{23} \text{ Na atoms}}{\text{mol } Na}$$

$$= 4.31 \times 10^{23} \text{ atoms } Na$$

c. Given: 6.59×10^{20} atoms Na

Unknown: number of molecules of H_2

number of molecules $H_2 = (6.59 \times 10^{20}$ atoms $Na) \times \dfrac{1 \text{ molecule } H_2}{2 \text{ atoms } Na}$

$$= 3.30 \times 10^{20} \text{ molecules } H_2$$

---

38. a. Given: 4.0 mol NO
4.0 mol O_2

$2NO + O_2 \rightarrow 2NO_2$

Unknown: excess reactant, limiting reactant

mass $NO_2 = 4.0$ mol $NO \times \dfrac{2 \text{ mol } NO_2}{2 \text{ mol } NO} \times \dfrac{46.01 \text{ g } NO_2}{\text{mol } NO_2}$

$$= 180 \text{ g } NO_2$$

mass $NO_2 = 4.0$ mol $O_2 \times \dfrac{2 \text{ mol } NO_2}{1 \text{ mol } O_2} \times \dfrac{46.01 \text{ g } NO_2}{\text{mol } NO_2}$

$$= 370 \text{ g } NO_2$$

Therefore, the excess reactant is O_2 and the limiting reactant is NO.

b. Unknown: theoretical yield of NO_2 (moles)

theoretical yield $NO_2 = 4.0$ mol $NO \times \dfrac{2 \text{ mol } NO_2}{2 \text{ mol } NO} = 4.0$ mol NO_2

---

39. a. Given: 64 g CaC_2
64 g H_2O

$CaC_2(s) + 2H_2O(l) \rightarrow C_2H_2(g) + Ca(OH)_2(s)$

Unknown: excess reactant, limiting reactant

mass $C_2H_2 = 64$ g $CaC_2 \times \dfrac{\text{mol } CaC_2}{64.01 \text{ g } CaC_2} \times \dfrac{1 \text{ mol } C_2H_2}{1 \text{ mol } CaC_2}$

$$\times \frac{26.04 \text{ g } C_2H_2}{\text{mol } C_2H_2}$$

$$= 26 \text{ g } C_2H_2$$

mass $C_2H_2 = 64$ g $H_2O \times \dfrac{\text{mol } H_2O}{18.02 \text{ g } H_2O} \times \dfrac{1 \text{ mol } C_2H_2}{2 \text{ mol } H_2O}$

$$\times \frac{26.04 \text{ g } C_2H_2}{\text{mol } C_2H_2}$$

$$= 46 \text{ g } C_2H_2$$

Therefore, the limiting reactant is CaC_2 and the excess reactant is H_2O.

b. Unknown: theoretical yield of C_2H_2

theoretical yield $C_2H_2 = 64$ g $CaC_2 \times \dfrac{\text{mol } CaC_2}{64.01 \text{ g } CaC_2} \times \dfrac{1 \text{ mol } C_2H_2}{1 \text{ mol } CaC_2}$

$$\times \dfrac{26.04 \text{ g } C_2H_2}{\text{mol } C_2H_2}$$

$$= 26 \text{ g } C_2H_2$$

c. Unknown: theoretical yield of $Ca(OH)_2$

theoretical yield $Ca(OH)_2 = 64$ g $CaC_2 \times \dfrac{\text{mol } CaC_2}{64.01 \text{ g } CaC_2}$

$$\times \dfrac{1 \text{ mol } Ca(OH)_2}{1 \text{ mol } CaC_2} \times \dfrac{74.10 \text{ g } Ca(OH)_2}{\text{mol } Ca(OH)_2}$$

$$= 74 \text{ g } Ca(OH)_2$$

40. a. Given: 28 g N_2
28 g H_2
$N_2(g) + 3H_2(g) \rightarrow$
$2NH_3(g)$

Unknown: excess reactant, limiting reactant

mass $NH_3 = 28$ g $N_2 \times \dfrac{\text{mol } N_2}{28.02 \text{ g } N_2} \times \dfrac{2 \text{ mol } NH_3}{1 \text{ mol } N_2} \times \dfrac{17.04 \text{ g } NH_3}{\text{mol } NH_3}$

$$= 34 \text{ g } NH_3$$

mass $NH_3 = 82$ g $H_2 \times \dfrac{\text{mol } H_2}{2.02 \text{ g } H_2} \times \dfrac{2 \text{ mol } NH_3}{3 \text{ mol } H_2} \times \dfrac{17.04 \text{ g } NH_3}{\text{mol } NH_3}$

$$= 160 \text{ g } NH_3$$

Therefore, N_2 is the limiting reactant and H_2 is the excess reactant.

b. Unknown: theoretical yield

theoretical yield $NH_3 = 28$ g $N_2 \times \dfrac{\text{mol } N_2}{28.02 \text{ g } N_2} \times \dfrac{2 \text{ mol } NH_3}{1 \text{ mol } N_2}$

$$\times \dfrac{17.04 \text{ g } NH_3}{\text{mol } NH_3}$$

$$= 34 \text{ g } NH_3$$

c. Unknown: mass excess reactant

mass excess reactant used $= 28$ g $N_2 \times \dfrac{1 \text{ mol } N_2}{28.02 \text{ g } N_2} \times \dfrac{3 \text{ mol } H_2}{1 \text{ mol } N_2}$

$$\times \dfrac{2.02 \text{ g } H_2}{\text{mol } H_2}$$

$$= 6.1 \text{ g } H_2 \text{ used}$$

mass remaining $= 28$ g $H_2 - 6.1$ g $H_2 = 22$ g H_2

41. Given: 991 mol SiO_2
excess carbon
30.0 kg SiC
$SiO_2 + 3C \rightarrow SiC + 2CO$

Unknown: percent yield

theoretical yield SiC $= 991$ mol $SiO_2 \times \dfrac{1 \text{ mol SiC}}{1 \text{ mol } SiO_2} \times \dfrac{40.09 \text{ g SiC}}{\text{mol SiC}}$

$$= 3.97 \times 10^4 \text{ g SiC}$$

$$\text{percent yield} = \dfrac{\text{actual yield}}{\text{theoretical yield}} \times 100$$

$$= \dfrac{30.0 \text{ kg SiC}}{3.97 \times 10^4 \text{ g SiC}} \times \dfrac{1000 \text{ g}}{\text{kg}} \times 100 = 75.6\%$$

42. Given: 156 g $NaNO_3$
112 g $NaNO_2$
$2NaNO_3 \rightarrow$
$\qquad 2NaNO_2 + O_2$
Unknown: percent yield

theoretical yield = 156 g $NaNO_3 \times \dfrac{\text{mol } NaNO_3}{85.00 \text{ g } NaNO_3}$

$\times \dfrac{2 \text{ mol } NaNO_2}{2 \text{ mol } NaNO_3} \times \dfrac{69.00 \text{ g } NaNO_2}{\text{mol } NaNO_2}$

$= 127$ g $NaNO_2$

percent yield = $\dfrac{\text{actual yield}}{\text{theoretical yield}} \times 100$

$= \dfrac{112 \text{ g } NaNO_2}{127 \text{ g } NaNO_2} \times 100 = 88.2\%$

43. Given: 185 g Mg
1000.0 g $MgCl_2$
Unknown: percent yield

balanced equation = $MgCl_2(s) \rightarrow Mg(s) + Cl_2(g)$

theoretical yield Mg = 1000.0 g $MgCl_2 \times \dfrac{\text{mol } MgCl_2}{95.21 \text{ g } MgCl_2}$

$\times \dfrac{1 \text{ mol Mg}}{1 \text{ mol } MgCl_2} \times \dfrac{24.31 \text{ g Mg}}{\text{mol Mg}}$

$= 255.3$ g Mg

percent yield = $\dfrac{\text{actual yield}}{\text{theoretical yield}} \times 100$

$= \dfrac{185 \text{ g Mg}}{255.3 \text{ g Mg}} \times 100 = 72.5\%$

44. Given: percent yield =
91%
256 g $NaNO_3$
$2NaNO_3(s) \rightarrow$
$2NaNO_2(s) + O_2(g)$
Unknown: mass $NaNO_2$

theoretical yield = 256 g $NaNO_3 \times \dfrac{\text{mol } NaNO_3}{85.00 \text{ g } NaNO_3}$

$\times \dfrac{2 \text{ mol } NaNO_2}{2 \text{ mol } NaNO_3} \times \dfrac{69.00 \text{ g } NaNO_2}{\text{mol } NaNO_2}$

$= 208$ g $NaNO_2$

actual yield = 208 g $NaNO_2 \times 0.91 = 1.9 \times 10^2$ g $NaNO_2$

45. Given: 9.73 g Al_2O_3
91% yield
$Al_2O_3 + 3C \rightarrow$
$\qquad 2Al + 3CO$
Unknown: mass Al

theoretical yield Al = 9.73 g $Al_2O_3 \times \dfrac{\text{mol } Al_2O_3}{101.96 \text{ g } Al_2O_3}$

$\times \dfrac{2 \text{ mol Al}}{1 \text{ mol } Al_2O_3} \times \dfrac{26.98 \text{ g Al}}{\text{mol Al}}$

$= 5.15$ g Al

actual yield = 5.15 g Al $\times 0.91 = 4.7$ g Al

46. Given: 4.56 kg Fe_2O_3
88% yield
Unknown: mass of Fe

balanced equation = $2Fe_2O_3 + 3C \rightarrow 4Fe + 3CO_2$

theoretical yield Fe = 4.56 kg $Fe_2O_3 \times \dfrac{1000 \text{ g}}{\text{kg}} \times \dfrac{\text{mol } Fe_2O_3}{159.70 \text{ g } Fe_2O_3}$

$\times \dfrac{4 \text{ mol Fe}}{2 \text{ mol } Fe_2O_3} \times \dfrac{55.85 \text{ g Fe}}{\text{mol Fe}}$

$= 3.19 \times 10^3$ g Fe

actual yield = $(3.19 \times 10^3$ g Fe$) \times \dfrac{\text{kg}}{1000 \text{ g}} \times 0.88 = 2.8$ kg Fe

47. Given: 44.3 g Na_2O
density CO_2 =
1.35 g/L
$Na_2O(s) + 2CO_2(g) + H_2O(g) \rightarrow 2NaHCO_3(s)$

Unknown: volume CO_2

$$\text{volume } CO_2 = 44.3 \text{ g } Na_2O \times \frac{\text{mol } Na_2O}{61.98 \text{ g } Na_2O} \times \frac{2 \text{ mol } CO_2}{1 \text{ mol } Na_2O}$$

$$\times \frac{44.01 \text{ g } CO_2}{\text{mol } CO_2} \times \frac{\text{L } CO_2}{1.35 \text{ g } CO_2} = 46.6 \text{ L } CO_2$$

---

48. a. Given: 59.5 L N_2
density N_2 =
0.92 g/L
$2NaN_3(s) \rightarrow 2Na(s) + 3N_2(g)$

Unknown: mass NaN_3

$$\text{mass } N_2 = 59.5 \text{ L } N_2 \times \frac{0.92 \text{ g } N_2}{\text{L } N_2} = 55 \text{ g } N_2$$

$$\text{mass } NaN_3 = 55 \text{ g } N_2 \times \frac{\text{mol } N_2}{28.02 \text{ g } N_2} \times \frac{2 \text{ mol } NaN_3}{3 \text{ mol } N_2} \times \frac{65.02 \text{ g } NaN_3}{\text{mol } NaN_3}$$

$$= 85 \text{ g } NaN_3$$

b. Given: 65.7 g NaN_3
actual yield = 94%

Unknown: volume of N_2 in L

$$65.7 \text{ g } NaN_3 \times \frac{\text{mol } NaN_3}{65.02 \text{ g } NaN_3} \times \frac{3 \text{ mol } N_2}{2 \text{ mol } NaN_3} \times \frac{28.02 \text{ g } N_2}{\text{mol } N_2}$$

$$\times \frac{\text{L } N_2}{0.92 \text{ g } N_2} = 46.2 \text{ L } N_2$$

$$46.2 \text{ L } N_2 \times 0.94 = 43.4 \text{ L } N_2$$

c. Given: 59.5 L N_2
actual yield = 94%

Unknown: mass of NaN_3

$$\frac{59.5 \text{ L } N_2}{\text{theoretical yield}} = 0.94$$

$$\text{theoretical yield} = \frac{59.5 \text{ L } N_2}{0.94} = 63 \text{ L } N_2$$

$$63 \text{ L } N_2 \times \frac{0.92 \text{ g } N_2}{\text{L } N_2} \times \frac{\text{mol } N_2}{28.02 \text{ g } N_2} \times \frac{2 \text{ mol } NaN_3}{3 \text{ mol } N_2} \times \frac{65.02 \text{ g } NaN_3}{\text{mol } NaN_3}$$

$$= 9.0 \times 10^1 \text{ g } NaN_3$$

---

50. Given: 688 g C_8H_{18}

Unknown: mass O_2

balanced equation = $2C_8H_{18} + 25O_2 \rightarrow 18H_2O + 16CO_2$

$$\text{mass } O_2 = 688 \text{ g } C_8H_{18} \times \frac{\text{mol } C_8H_{18}}{114.26 \text{ g } C_8H_{18}} \times \frac{25 \text{ mol } O_2}{2 \text{ mol } C_8H_{18}}$$

$$\times \frac{32.00 \text{ g } O_2}{\text{mol } O_2}$$

$$= 2.41 \times 10^3 \text{ g } C_8H_{18}$$

---

51. Given: density O_2 =
1.43 g/L
1.00 L C_8H_{18}
density C_8H_{18} =
0.700 g/mL

Unknown: volume O_2

$2C_8H_{18} + 25O_2 \rightarrow 18H_2O + 16CO_2$

$$\text{mass } C_8H_{18} = 1.00 \text{ L } C_8H_{18} \times \frac{1000 \text{ mL}}{\text{L}} \times \frac{0.700 \text{ g } C_8H_{18}}{\text{mL } C_8H_{18}}$$

$$= 700 \text{ g } C_8H_{18}$$

$$\text{volume } O_2 = 700 \text{ g } C_8H_{18} \times \frac{\text{mol } C_8H_{18}}{114.26 \text{ g } C_8H_{18}} \times \frac{25 \text{ mol } O_2}{2 \text{ mol } C_8H_{18}}$$

$$\times \frac{32.00 \text{ g } O_2}{\text{mol } O_2} \times \frac{\text{L } O_2}{1.43 \text{ g } O_2} = 1.71 \times 10^3 \text{ L } O_2$$

---

52. Given: 4.55 g NO_2
4.58 g O_3
$NO_2(g) + O_2(g) \rightarrow$
$NO(g) + O_3(g)$

Unknown: mass O_2,
percent yield

mass $O_3 = 4.55$ g $NO_2 \times \dfrac{\text{mol } NO_2}{46.01 \text{ g } NO_2} \times \dfrac{1 \text{ mol } O_3}{1 \text{ mol } NO_2} \times \dfrac{48.00 \text{ g } O_3}{\text{mol } O_3}$

$= 4.75$ g O_3

percent yield $= \dfrac{\text{actual yield}}{\text{theoretical yield}} \times 100$

$= \dfrac{4.58 \text{ g } O_3}{4.75 \text{ g } O_3} \times 100 = 96.4\%$

53. Given: 1.00 L C_8H_{18}
density $C_8H_{18} =$
0.700 g/mL
1.90×10^3 g CO_2

Unknown: mass CO_2

mass $C_8H_{18} = 1.00$ L $C_8H_{18} \times \dfrac{1000 \text{ mL}}{L} \times \dfrac{0.700 \text{ g } C_8H_{18}}{\text{mL } C_8H_{18}}$

$= 700$ g C_8H_{18}

mass $CO_2 = 700$ g $C_8H_{18} \times \dfrac{\text{mol } C_8H_{18}}{114.26 \text{ g } C_8H_{18}} \times \dfrac{16 \text{ mol } CO_2}{2 \text{ mol } C_8H_{18}}$

$\times \dfrac{44.01 \text{ g } CO_2}{\text{mol } CO_2}$

$= 2.16 \times 10^3$ g CO_2

percent yield $= \dfrac{\text{actual yield}}{\text{theoretical yield}} \times 100$

$= \dfrac{1.90 \times 10^3 \text{ g } CO_2}{2.16 \times 10^3 \text{ g } CO_2} \times 100 = 88.0\%$

54. a. Given: 5.5 moles LiOH
$2LiOH(s) + CO_2(g) \rightarrow$
$Li_2CO_3(s) + H_2O(l)$

Unknown: mass CO_2

mass $CO_2 = 5.5$ mol LiOH $\times \dfrac{1 \text{ mol } CO_2}{2 \text{ mol LiOH}} \times \dfrac{44.01 \text{ g } CO_2}{\text{mol } CO_2}$

$= 1.2 \times 10^2$ g CO_2

b. Given: density $H_2O =$
0.997 g/mL
25.7 g LiOH

Unknown: volume
H_2O

mass $H_2O = 25.7$ g LiOH $\times \dfrac{\text{mol LiOH}}{23.95 \text{ g LiOH}} \times \dfrac{1 \text{ mol } H_2O}{2 \text{ mol LiOH}}$

$\times \dfrac{18.02 \text{ g } H_2O}{\text{mol } H_2O}$

$= 9.67$ g H_2O

volume $H_2O = 9.67$ g $H_2O \times \dfrac{\text{mL } H_2O}{0.997 \text{ g } H_2O} = 9.70$ mL H_2O

c. Given: 3.28 g CO_2

Unknown: number of
molecules
of H_2O

number of molecules $H_2O = 3.28$ g $CO_2 \times \dfrac{\text{mol } CO_2}{44.01 \text{ g } CO_2}$

$\times \dfrac{1 \text{ mol } H_2O}{1 \text{ mol } CO_2}$

$\times \dfrac{6.022 \times 10^{23} \text{ molecules } H_2O}{\text{mol } H_2O}$

$= 4.49 \times 10^{22}$ molecules H_2O

55. b. Given: 2.7 mol NaN_3
$2NaN_3(s) \rightarrow$
$2Na(s) + 3N_2(g)$

Unknown: amount N_2

amount $N_2 = 2.7$ mol $NaN_3 \times \dfrac{3 \text{ mol } N_2}{2 \text{ mol } NaN_3} = 4.0$ mol N_2

Solutions Manual *continued*

c. Given: 31.1 g NaN$_3$
Unknown: mass Na

$$\text{mass Na} = 31.1 \text{ g NaN}_3 \times \frac{\text{mol NaN}_3}{65.02 \text{ g NaN}_3} \times \frac{2 \text{ mol Na}}{2 \text{ mol NaN}_3}$$

$$\times \frac{22.99 \text{ g Na}}{\text{mol Na}}$$

$$= 11.0 \text{ g Na}$$

d. Given: 3.24×10^{23}
atoms Na

Unknown: number of
molecules
of N$_2$

$$\text{number of molecules N}_2 = (3.24 \times 10^{23} \text{ atoms}) \times \frac{3 \text{ molecules N}_2}{2 \text{Na atoms}}$$

$$= 4.86 \times 10^{23} \text{ molecules N}_2$$

---

56. a. Given: 55 g NO
35 g O$_2$
31 g NO$_2$
density NO =
1.3388 g/L
density NO$_2$ =
2.053 g/L
$2NO(g) + O_2(g) \rightarrow 2NO_2(g)$

Unknown: limiting
reactant

$$\text{mass NO}_2 = 55 \text{ g NO} \times \frac{\text{mol NO}}{30.01 \text{ g NO}} \times \frac{2 \text{ mol NO}_2}{2 \text{ mol NO}} \times \frac{46.01 \text{ g NO}_2}{\text{mol NO}_2}$$

$$= 84 \text{ g NO}_2$$

$$\text{mass NO}_2 = 35 \text{ g O}_2 \times \frac{\text{mol O}_2}{32.00 \text{ g O}_2} \times \frac{2 \text{ mol NO}_2}{1 \text{ mol O}_2} \times \frac{46.01 \text{ g NO}_2}{\text{mol NO}_2}$$

$$= 100 \text{ g NO}_2$$

$\therefore$ the limiting reactant is NO.

b. Unknown: theoretical
yield

$$\text{theoretical yield} = 55 \text{ g NO} \times \frac{\text{mol NO}}{30.01 \text{ g NO}} \times \frac{2 \text{ mol NO}_2}{2 \text{ mol NO}}$$

$$\times \frac{46.01 \text{ g NO}_2}{\text{mol NO}_2}$$

$$= 84 \text{ g NO}_2$$

c. Unknown: percent
yield

$$\text{percent yield} = \frac{\text{actual yield}}{\text{theoretical yield}} \times 100$$

$$= \frac{31 \text{ g NO}_2}{84 \text{ g NO}_2} \times 100 = 37.0\%$$

---

57. Given: density N$_2$ =
0.92 g/L
2.05 g NaN$_3$
$2NaN_3(s) \rightarrow 2Na(s) + 3N_2(g)$
Unknown: volume N$_2$

$$\text{volume N}_2 = 2.05 \text{ g NaN}_3 \times \frac{\text{mol NaN}_3}{65.02 \text{ g NaN}_3} \times \frac{3 \text{ mol N}_2}{2 \text{ mol NaN}_3}$$

$$\times \frac{28.02 \text{ g N}_2}{\text{mol N}_2} \times \frac{\text{L N}_2}{0.92 \text{ g N}_2} = 1.4 \text{ L N}_2$$

---

58. Given: percent yield =
95%
9.88 kg NO$_2$
$3NO_2(g) + H_2O(g) \rightarrow$
$2HNO_3(aq) + NO(g)$
Unknown: mass HNO$_3$

$$\text{mass HNO}_3 = 9.88 \text{ kg NO}_2 \times \frac{1000 \text{ g}}{\text{kg}} \times \frac{\text{mol NO}_2}{46.01 \text{ g NO}_2}$$

$$\times \frac{2 \text{ mol HNO}_3}{3 \text{ mol NO}_2} \times \frac{63.02 \text{ g HNO}_3}{\text{mol HNO}_3}$$

$$= 9.02 \times 10^3 \text{ g HNO}_3$$

$$9.02 \times 10^3 \text{ g HNO}_3 \times 0.95 \text{ yield} = 8.6 \times 10^3 \text{ g HNO}_3$$

59. Given: 25.3 mi/gal
5.4 mi
gal = 3.79 L
density C_8H_{18} =
0.700 g/L
Unknown: mass CO_2

$2C_8H_{18} + 25O_2 \rightarrow 18H_2O + 16CO_2$

$5.4 \text{ mi} \times \dfrac{\text{gal } C_8H_{18}}{25.3 \text{ mi}} \times \dfrac{3.79 \text{ L } C_8H_{18}}{\text{gal } C_8H_{18}} \times \dfrac{1000 \text{ mL}}{\text{L}}$

$\times \dfrac{0.700 \text{ g } C_8H_{18}}{\text{mL } C_8H_{18}} \times \dfrac{\text{mol } C_8H_{18}}{114.26 \text{ g } C_8H_{18}} \times \dfrac{16 \text{ mol } CO_2}{2 \text{ mol } C_8H_{18}}$

$\times \dfrac{44.01 \text{ g } CO_2}{\text{mol } CO_2} = 1.74 \times 10^3 \text{ g } CO_2$

60. Given: 4.55 g NO
Unknown: theoretical
yield O_3

balanced equations = $2NO + O_2 \rightarrow 2NO_2$
$NO_2 + O_2 \rightarrow NO + O_3$

theoretical yield $NO_2 = 4.55 \text{ g NO} \times \dfrac{\text{mol NO}}{30.01 \text{ g NO}} \times \dfrac{2 \text{ mol } NO_2}{2 \text{ mol NO}}$

$\times \dfrac{46.01 \text{ g } NO_2}{\text{mol } NO_2}$

$= 6.98 \text{ g } NO_2$

theoretical yield $O_3 = 6.98 \text{ g } NO_2 \times \dfrac{\text{mol } NO_2}{46.01 \text{ g } NO_2} \times \dfrac{1 \text{ mol } O_3}{1 \text{ mol } NO_2}$

$\times \dfrac{48 \text{ g } O_3}{\text{mol } O_3}$

$= 7.28 \text{ g } O_3$

67. Given: 25 mi/gal
density C_8H_{18} =
0.700 g/mL
1 gal = 3.79 L
1.20×10^4 mi/y
Unknown: theoretical
yield CO_2

$2C_8H_{18} + 25O_2 \rightarrow 16CO_2 + 18H_2O$

$\dfrac{9.00 \times 10^3 \text{ mi}}{y} \times \dfrac{\text{gal } C_8H_{18}}{25 \text{ mi}} \times \dfrac{3.79 \text{ L } C_8H_{18}}{\text{gal } C_8H_{18}} \times \dfrac{1000 \text{ mL}}{\text{L}}$

$\times \dfrac{0.700 \text{ g } C_8H_{18}}{\text{mL } C_8H_{18}} \times \dfrac{\text{mol } C_8H_{18}}{114.26 \text{ g } C_8H_{18}} \times \dfrac{16 \text{ mol } CO_2}{2 \text{ mol } C_8H_{18}}$

$\times \dfrac{44.01 \text{ g } CO_2}{\text{mol } CO_2} = 3.0 \times 10^6 \text{ g } CO_2/y$

Problem Bank

1. Given: solute = $CaCO_3$
solvent = HCl
products = CO_2;
$CaCl_2$, H_2
volume of CO_2 =
1500 mL $\dfrac{\text{L}}{1000 \text{ mL}}$
= 1.5 L
Unknown: mass of $CaCO_3$
in g

$CaCO_3(s) + 2HCl(aq) \rightarrow BaCl_2(aq) + H_2O(l) + CO_2(g)$

$(1.5 \text{ L } CO_2)\dfrac{\text{mol } CO_2}{22.4 \text{ L } CO_2} \dfrac{1 \text{ mol } CaCO_3}{1 \text{ mol } CO_2}$

$= 0.067 \text{ mol } CaCO_3$

$(0.067 \text{ mol } CaCO_3)\dfrac{100.0 \text{ g } CaCO_3}{\text{mol } CaCO_3}$

$= 6.7 \text{ g } CaCO_3$

2. Given: mass of SO_2

$= (3.50 \times 10^8 \text{ kg}) \dfrac{1000 \text{ g}}{\text{kg}}$

$= 3.50 \times 10^{11} \text{ g}$

$SO_2 + \dfrac{1}{2}O_2 \rightarrow SO_3$

$SO_3 + H_2O \rightarrow H_2SO_4$

Unknown: mass of H_2SO_4 produced in kg

$3.50 \times 10^{11} \text{ g } SO_2 \times \dfrac{\text{mol } SO_2}{64.1 \text{ g } SO_2} \dfrac{1 \text{ mol } SO_3}{1 \text{ mol } SO_2}$

$= 5.46 \times 10^9 \text{ mol } SO_3$

$5.46 \times 10^9 \text{ mol } SO_3 \times \dfrac{1 \text{ mol } H_2SO_4}{1 \text{ mol } SO_3}$

$\times \dfrac{98.1 \text{ g } H_2SO_4}{\text{mol } H_2SO_4} \dfrac{\text{kg}}{1000 \text{ g}}$

$= 5.36 \times 10^8 \text{ kg } H_2SO_4$

---

3. a. Given: $V = 0.750$ L $H_2O(g)$ at STP

Unknown: number of grams $Fe(OH)_3$ used

$2Fe(OH)_3(s) \rightarrow Fe_2O_3(s) + 3H_2O(g)$

$n = (0.750 \text{ L}H_2O)\left(\dfrac{1 \text{ mol } H_2O}{22.4 \text{ L}}\right)$

$\times \left(\dfrac{2 \text{ mol } Fe(OH)_3}{3 \text{ mol } H_2O}\right)$

$= 0.0223214 \text{ mol } Fe(OH)_3$

$m = (0.0223214 \text{ mol})\left(\dfrac{106.8 \text{ g } Fe(OH)_3}{\text{mol}}\right)$

$= 2.38 \text{ g } Fe(OH)_3$

b. Given: $V = 0.750$ L $H_2O(g)$ at STP

Unknown: number of grams Fe_2O_3 used

$n = (0.750 \text{ L}H_2O)\left(\dfrac{1 \text{ mol } H_2O}{22.4 \text{ L}}\right)$

$\times \left(\dfrac{1 \text{ mol } Fe_2O_3}{3 \text{ mol } H_2O}\right)$

$= 0.0111607 \text{ mol } Fe_2O_3$

$m = (0.0111607 \text{ mol})\left(\dfrac{159.6 \text{ g } Fe(OH)_3}{\text{mol}}\right)$

$= 1.78 \text{ g } Fe_2O_3$

---

4. a. Given: conditions are at STP

V of $O_2 = 22.4$ L

Unknown: moles of MgO produced

$2Mg(s) + O_2(g) \rightarrow 2MgO(s)$

$(22.4 \text{ L } O_2)\left(\dfrac{1.00 \text{ mol}}{22.4 \text{ L}}\right) = 1 \text{ mol } O_2$

$(1 \text{ mol})\left(\dfrac{2 \text{ mol } MgO}{1 \text{ mol } O_2}\right) = 2 \text{ mol } MgO$

b. Given: conditions are at STP

V of $O_2 = 11.2$ L

Unknown: moles of MgO produced

$2Mg(s) + O_2(g) \rightarrow 2MgO(s)$

$(11.2 \text{ L } O_2)\left(\dfrac{1.00 \text{ mol}}{22.4 \text{ L}}\right) = 0.5 \text{ mol } O_2$

$(0.5 \text{ mol})\left(\dfrac{2 \text{ mol } MgO}{1 \text{ mol } O_2}\right) = 1 \text{ mol } MgO$

c. Given: conditions are at STP

V of $O_2 = 1.40$ L

Unknown: moles of MgO produced

$2Mg(s) + O_2(g) \rightarrow 2MgO(s)$

$(1.40 \text{ L } O_2)\left(\dfrac{1.00 \text{ mol}}{22.4 \text{ L}}\right) = 0.0625 \text{ mol } O_2$

$(0.0625 \text{ mol})\left(\dfrac{2 \text{ mol } MgO}{1 \text{ mol } O_2}\right) = 0.125 \text{ mol } MgO$

---

5. a. Given: $V = 8.50$ L I_2 at STP

Unknown: number of moles I_2 produced

$2KI(aq) + Cl_2(g) \rightarrow 2KCl(aq) + I_2(g)$

$n = (8.50 \text{ L } I_2)\left(\dfrac{\text{mol } I_2}{22.4 \text{ L } I_2}\right)$

$= 0.379 \text{ mol } I_2$

b. Unknown: number of moles KI used

$n = (0.379 \text{ mol } I_2)\left(\dfrac{2 \text{ mol KI}}{1 \text{ mol } I_2}\right)$

$= 0.758 \text{ mol KI}$

c. Unknown: number of grams KI used

$m = (0.758 \text{ mol KI})\left(\dfrac{166 \text{ g KI}}{\text{mol}}\right)$

$= 126 \text{ g KI}$

6. Given: $V = 650$ mL H_2 produced at STP

Unknown: number of g of $FeSO_4$ produced

$Fe(s) + H_2SO_4 \rightarrow FeSO_4 + H_2$

$(650.0 \text{ mL})\left(\dfrac{\text{L}}{1000 \text{ mL}}\right) = 0.650 \text{ L}$

$(0.650 \text{ L } H_2)\left(\dfrac{\text{mol } H_2}{22.4 \text{ L}}\right) = 0.0290179 \text{ mol } H_2$

$(0.0290179 \text{ mol } H_2)\left(\dfrac{1 \text{ mol } FeSO_4}{1 \text{ mol } H_2}\right)$

$= 0.0290179 \text{ mol } FeSO_4$

$(0.0290179 \text{ mol } FeSO_4)\left(\dfrac{151.9 \text{ g } FeSO_4}{1 \text{ mol } FeSO_4}\right)$

$= 4.41 \text{ g } FeSO_4$

7. a. Given: $V = 450$ mL CO
$V = 825$ mL H_2

Unknown: reactant present in excess

$CO(g) + 2H_2(g) \rightarrow CH_3OH(g)$

$(825 \text{ mL } H_2)\left(\dfrac{1 \text{ mL CO}}{2 \text{ mL } H_2}\right) = 412.5 \text{ mL}$

CO is present in excess. (450 mL > 412.5 mL)

b. Unknown: amount of CO remaining after reaction

$450 \text{ mL} - 412.5 \text{ mL} = 38 \text{ mL CO}$

c. Unknown: volume of CH_3OH produced

$(825 \text{ mL})\left(\dfrac{1 \text{ mL } CH_3OH}{2 \text{ mL } H_2}\right)$

$= 412 \text{ mL } CH_3OH$